Name: _____

GL

Verbal Reasoning

11+ Practice Papers

Alison Head

GALORE PARK

AN HACHETTE UK COMPANY

GL Assessment produces annual and bespoke 11+ tests for a range of schools and does not make past papers available to pupils. However, the feedback from our specialist team of 11+ tutors, independent schools' teachers, test writers and specialist authors enables us to provide you with a series of tests equipping your child with the highest level preparation. This publication covers standard question types representative of the GL range of assessments, tracking trends and levels of difficulty from the last several years. Tests can change from year to year and there is therefore no guarantee that all question types your child will encounter are represented in this publication.

Every effort has been made to trace all copyright holders, but if any have been inadvertently overlooked, the Publishers will be pleased to make the necessary arrangements at the first opportunity.

Although every effort has been made to ensure that website addresses are correct at time of going to press, Galore Park cannot be held responsible for the content of any website mentioned in this book. It is sometimes possible to find a relocated web page by typing in the address of the home page for a website in the URL window of your browser.

Hachette UK's policy is to use papers that are natural, renewable and recyclable products and made from wood grown in well-managed forests and other controlled sources. The logging and manufacturing processes are expected to conform to the environmental regulations of the country of origin.

Orders: **Teachers** please contact Bookpoint Ltd, 130 Park Drive, Milton Park, Abingdon, Oxon OX14 4SE. Telephone: (44) 01235 400555. Email primary@bookpoint.co.uk. Lines are open from 9 a.m. to 5 p.m., Monday to Saturday, with a 24-hour message answering service.

Parents, Tutors please call: 020 3122 6405 (Monday to Friday, 9:30 a.m. to 4.30 p.m.). Email: parentenquiries@galorepark.co.uk

Visit our website at www.galorepark.co.uk for details of other revision guides for Common Entrance, examination papers and Galore Park publications.

ISBN: **978 1 5104 4977 0**

© Alison Head 2019
First published in 2019 by
Hodder & Stoughton Limited
An Hachette UK Company
Carmelite House
50 Victoria Embankment
London EC4Y 0DZ
www.galorepark.co.uk
Impression number   10 9 8 7 6 5 4 3 2 1
Year 2023 2022 2021 2020 2019

Typeset in India
Printed in the UK

A catalogue record for this title is available from the British Library.

Contents and progress record

Page	Length (no. Qs)	Timing (mins)	Question type	Score	Time
Paper 1 Foundation level Representing a GL test at an average level of challenge for grammar and independent schools.					
7	80	60	Multiple choice	**/ 80**	:
Paper 2 Standard level Representing a GL test at a medium level of challenge for grammar and independent schools.					
15	80	60	Multiple choice	**/ 80**	:
Paper 3 Standard / advanced level Representing a GL test at a medium to high level of challenge for grammar and independent schools.					
23	80	60	Multiple choice	**/ 80**	:
Paper 4 Advanced level Representing a GL test at a high level of challenge for independent schools.					
34	80	45	Multiple choice	**/ 80**	:

Go to the Galore Park website to download the free PDF answer sheets to use and re-use as many times as you need: galorepark.co.uk/answersheets

How to use this book

Introduction

These practice papers have been written to provide final preparation for your GL 11+ verbal reasoning test. To give you the best chance of success, Galore Park has worked with 11+ tutors, independent schools' teachers, test writers and specialist authors to create these practice papers.

This book includes four model papers. Each paper contains 80 multiple-choice questions, covering a variety of skills. The papers increase in difficulty from Paper 1 to Paper 4 and all work to a timing that has been typical of GL tests in the past. This is because GL tests can change in difficulty both from year to year and from school to school. Because each paper differs slightly in complexity and skill area, we suggest you complete all four papers to help you fully prepare for the challenges ahead.

You are asked to record your answers using a separate answer sheet. As you mark your answers, you will see references to the Galore Park *11+ Verbal Reasoning Study and Revision Guide*. These references have been included so that you can go straight to some useful revision tips and find extra practice questions for those areas where you would like more help.

Working through the book

The **Contents and progress record** on page 3 helps you to track your scores and timings as you work through the papers.

You may find some of the questions hard, but don't worry – these tests are designed to make you think. Agree with your parents on a good time to take the test and follow the instructions below to prepare for each paper as if you are actually going to sit your Pre-test/11+ verbal reasoning test.

1 Download the **answer sheet** from www.galorepark.co.uk/answersheets and print it out before you begin.
2 Take the test in a quiet room. Set a timer and record your answers as instructed.
3 Note down how long the paper takes you (you should complete all questions even if you run over the time suggested). If possible, complete a whole paper in one session.
4 Mark the paper using the answers at the back of the book.
5 Go through the paper again with a friend or parent, talk about the difficult questions and note which parts of the revision guide you are going to review.

The **Answers** can be cut out so that you can mark your papers easily. Do not look at the answers until you have attempted a whole paper.

When you have finished a paper, turn back to the **Contents and progress record** and fill in the **Score** and **Time** boxes.

If you would like to take further GL-style papers after completing this book, you will find more papers in the *Pre-test/11+ Verbal Reasoning Practice Papers 1* and *2* (see **Continue your learning journey** on page 6).

Pre-test and the 11+ entrance exams

This title is part of the Galore Park *Pre-test/11+* series and there are three further *Verbal Reasoning Practice Paper* titles (see **Continue your learning journey** on page 6).

This series is designed to help you prepare for pre-tests and 11+ entrance exams if you are applying to independent schools. These exams are often the same as those set by local grammar schools.

Pre-tests and 11+ verbal reasoning tests appear in a variety of formats and lengths and it is likely that if you are applying for more than one school, you will encounter more than one of style of test. These include:

● Pre-test/11+ entrance exams in different formats from GL, CEM and ISEB
● Pre-test/11+ entrance exams created specifically for particular schools.

As the tests change all the time it can be difficult to predict the questions, making them harder to revise for. If you are taking more than one style of test, review the books in the **Continue your learning journey** section to see which other titles could be helpful to you.

For parents

For your child to get the maximum benefit from these papers, they should complete them in conditions as close as possible to those they will face in the actual test, as described in the **Working through the book** section on page 4.

Working with your child to follow up the revision work suggested in the answers can improve their performance in areas where they are less confident and boost their chances of success.

For teachers and tutors

As the papers get progressively more difficult, they offer practice in increasing speed at answering questions required in the most challenging verbal reasoning tests.

The answer sheets provide helpful practice in recording answers on a separate document.

Remediation suggested in the answers, referencing the *Revision Guide*, can be helpful for follow-up revision having completed the paper.

Continue your learning journey

When you have completed these *Practice Papers*, you can carry on your learning right up until exam day with the following resources.

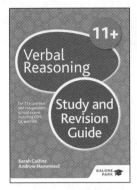   

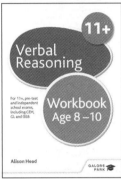 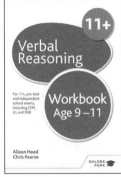 

The *Revision Guide* (referenced in the answers to this book) reviews basic skills in all areas of verbal reasoning, and guidance is provided on how to improve in this subject.

Pre-test/11+ Practice Papers 1 and *2* are designed to provide a complete revision experience across the various test styles you may encounter. Between the two titles there are eighteen tests of varying lengths, each followed by comprehensive answer explanations.

- *Book 1* begins with four training tests, followed by four short papers and two longer format papers designed to develop your confidence and speed.
- *Book 2* contains a further eight model papers and answers to improve your accuracy, speed and ability to deal with variations in question format under pressure.

CEM 11+ Verbal Reasoning & Cloze Procedure Practice Papers contains four practice papers designed for preparation for the CEM-style tests. Each paper is split into short tests in verbal reasoning and cloze procedure. The tests vary in length and format and are excellent for short bursts of timed practice.

The *Workbooks* will further develop your skills with over 220 questions to practise in each book. To prepare you for the exam, these books include more examples of the question variations contained in the *Practice Papers* – the more times you practise the questions, the better equipped for the exams you'll be.

- Age 8–10: Increase your familiarity with variations in the question types.
- Age 9–11: Experiment with further techniques to improve your accuracy.
- Age 10–12: Develop faster response times through consistent practice.

Use Atom Learning to improve familiarity with online tests: the online learning platform adapts to your ability to ensure you are always working on your optimal learning path and the adaptive, mock-testing facility looks and scores in the style of the pre-tests.

galorepark.co.uk/atomlearning

 # Paper 1

Download and print the answer sheet from galorepark.co.uk/answersheets before you start this paper.

Find a common letter

Find *one* letter that will complete the first word and begin the second word in both pairs. The same letter must be added to *both* sets of brackets. Follow the example to answer the questions, then mark the answers on the answer sheet.

> ### Example
> ho [?] op   pa [?] ame
>
> **a** p   **b** d   **c** t   **d** g   **e** n
>
> Answer: **c t**
>
> ho [t] op   pa [t] ame
>
> By adding the letter 't' to both sets of brackets, you make four news words: **hot, top, pat, tame.**

1   wi [?] rip   fa [?] our   (1)
    a w   b t   c n   d o   e g

2   ow [?] end   mea [?] id   (1)
    a t   b n   c r   d e   e l

3   lo [?] an   moa [?] ap   (1)
    a w   b n   c p   d t   e l

4   ap [?] ar   fle [?] arn   (1)
    a b   b e   c t   d d   e o

5   har [?] our   sa [?] ost   (1)
    a m   b t   c d   d p   e e

6   ba [?] ug   gai [?] ear   (1)
    a n   b r   c t   d l   e g

7   hal [?] end   lea [?] ail   (1)
    a l   b t   c f   d m   e d

Find the hidden word

Find a word, made up of four letters, that crosses two other words. Follow the example to answer the questions, then mark the answers on the answer sheet.

> ## Example
> Hannah tipped the contents of her purse all around the desk.
>
> **a**   Hannah tipped   **b** tipped the   **c** her purse   **d** purse all   **e** the desk
>
> Answer: **d** purse all   seal
>
> Hannah tipped the contents of her pur|se all| around the desk.

8   Our new rabbit has very big ears.   (1)

    a   Our new   **b**   rabbit has   **c**   has very   **d**   very big   **e**   big ears

9   I looked with envy at the cake.   (1)

    a   I looked   **b**   looked with   **c**   with envy   **d**   envy at   **e**   at the

10 Dad sliced the apple carefully into pieces.   (1)

    a   Dad sliced   **b**   sliced the   **c**   the apple   **d**   apple carefully   **e**   into pieces

11 My three little cousins always look for food.   (1)

    a   three little   **b**   little cousins   **c**   cousins always   **d**   always look   **e**   for food

12 Last year I gave all my old school books away.   (1)

    a   Last year   **b**   gave all   **c**   all my   **d**   my old   **e**   books away

13 All the snow was cleared by local men and women.   (1)

    a   the snow   **b**   was cleared   **c**   cleared by   **d**   local men   **e**   and women

14 The huge table was covered in many delicious foods.   (1)

    a   The huge   **b**   table was   **c**   covered in   **d**   many delicious   **e**   delicious foods

Synonyms

Find two words, one from each set of brackets, that are *most similar* in meaning. Follow the example to answer the questions, then mark the answers on the answer sheet.

> ## Example
> (**a** slip   **b** jump   **c** leap)   (**x** skip   **y** slide   **z** step)
>
> Answer: **a** slip, **y** slide
>
> Both 'slip' and 'slide' mean to slither – 'jump' and 'leap' are synonyms (words with similar meanings) but in the same set of brackets so cannot be selected.

15 (a bring   b tear   c follow)   (x trip   y rip   z shelter)   (1)

16 (a danger   b safety   c fall)   (x advice   y peril   z careful)   (1)

17 (a anger   b howl   c sad)   (x shout   y whisper   z rush)   (1)

18 (a collect   b conceal   c preserve)   (x reveal   y secrete   z find)   (1)

19 (a foolish   b funny   c wisdom)   (x cautious   y absurd   z dangerous)   (1)

20 (a perfect   b flaw   c wreck)   (x accuse   y fail   z fault)   (1)

21 (a shy   b quiet   c hidden)   (x faint   y mild   z timid)   (1)

22 (a frustrated   b impatient   c nervous)   (x confident   y discouraged   z determined)   (1)

Statement logic

Read the following statements:

Ben, Mara, Lucy and Nesaar are planning their weekend together.

Ben and Lucy like going to the cinema best.

Mara and Nesaar enjoy bowling.

Nesaar suggests ice skating and Ben thinks it is a good idea.

Mara has not been ice skating recently.

23 If the statements above are true, this must mean that only *one* of the following statements can be *true*. Which one? Mark the answer on the answer sheet. (1)

    a   Ben and Lucy hate bowling.

    b   Lucy prefers the cinema to bowling.

    c   Nesaar does not like the cinema.

    d   Ben does not like bowling.

    e   Mara has more experience of bowling than ice skating.

Word relationships

The middle word in the first triplet has been made from letters taken from the other two words in the triplet. Identify which letters were used to make it and apply the same pattern to complete the second triplet. The answer must be a proper word. Follow the example to answer the questions, then mark the answers on the answer sheet.

Example

chat (late) lend   dear (...) west

a wear   **b** wart   c send   **d** teas   e ware

Answer: **e** ware

c h a t   (l a t e) l e n d   d e a r   (w a r e) w e s t

1 2 3 4   (5 3 4 6) 5 6 7 8   1 2 3 4   (5 3 4 6) 5 6 7 8

24 beak (kept) port   raft (...) lake (1)

    a   late   b   rake   c   rote   d   tale   e   fake

25 folk (loaf) star   tack (...) warm (1)

    a   wart   b   cart   c   rack   d   cram   e   tram

26 ship (spin) oven   tear (...) soup (1)

    a   reap   b   pear   c   star   d   part   e   trap

27 ghost (stoke) speck   teeth (...) clear (1)

    a   lacer   b   there   c   three   d   heath   e   treat

28 bleak (black) clunk   steer (...) alarm (1)

    a   alerts   b   meats   c   reels   d   steam   e   steel

29 learn (bread) bride   bumps (...) slope (1)

    a   plump   b   slump   c   lopes   d   soups   e   mopes

30 reasons (restore) skaters   student (...) analyst (1)

    a   assists   b   stylist   c   dentist   d   stalest   e   stunted

Move a single letter

Make two new words by moving one letter from the first word and adding it to the second, without moving any other letters. Follow the example to answer the questions, then mark the answers on the answer sheet.

31 space   tin   (1)

    a s   b p   c a   d c   e e

32 sting   fee   (1)

    a s   b t   c i   d n   e g

33 block   one   (1)

    a b   b l   c o   d c   e k

34 niece   clan   (1)

    a n   b i   c e   d c   e e

35 brawn   tine   (1)

    a b   b r   c a   d w   e n

36 paint   stem   (1)

    a p   b a   c i   d n   e t

37 women   net   (1)

    a w   b o   c m   d e   e n

Spot the difference

Identify the *two* words that do not belong with the other three in these sets of words. Follow the example to answer the questions, then mark the answers on the answer sheet.

38	a purple	b bright	c blue	d grey	e plain	(1)
39	a toe	b sock	c ankle	d foot	e boot	(1)
40	a apple	b carrot	c banana	d grape	e onion	(1)
41	a soft	b touch	c sight	d image	e taste	(1)
42	a root	b soil	c branch	d leaf	e grow	(1)
43	a night	b star	c planet	d moon	e dark	(1)
44	a own	b demand	c possess	d desire	e have	(1)
45	a keen	b eager	c sharp	d avid	e astute	(1)

Complete the sentence

Three letters have been removed from the word in capital letters. If they are kept in the same order, these three letters spell another word. Follow the example to answer the questions, then mark the answers on the answer sheet.

46 My baby brother was born in the HOSAL.   (1)

     a PAT   b PIT   c SIT   d TAN   e ORB

47 Our journey lasted three HS.   (1)

     a AIR   b ORE   c OUR   d OAT   e AID

48 I SPED on the icy path.   (1)

     a IMP   b LAP   c CAR   d LIP   e ATE

49 We made an AGREET.   (1)

     a ONE   b NET   c MEN   d MAN   e ATE

50 Our rabbit ESED.   (1)

     a GOT   b EAT   c LOP   d CAP   e DIP

51 Dad had a FL of coffee.   (1)

     a OAT   b ARK   c ASK   d ARE   e OAR

52 I love BING   (1)

     a BEE   b ORE   c ATE   d EEL   e OWL

Match the meaning

Choose *one* word from the list that has a link with the words in both sets of brackets. Follow the example to answer the questions, then mark the answers on the answer sheet.

53 (pole, stake)   (mail, letters)   (1)

    a support   **b** prop   **c** post   **d** stamp   **e** ring

54 (piece, section)   (divide, separate)   (1)

    a patch   **b** part   **c** pitch   **d** join   **e** place

55 (select, choose)   (gather, harvest)   (1)

    a put   **b** pull   **c** opt   **d** order   **e** pick

56 (strike, hit)   (rhythm, tempo)   (1)

    a drill   **b** pound   **c** drum   **d** beat   **e** hammer

57 (beloved, treasured)   (costly, expensive)   (1)

    a rare   **b** dear   **c** value   **d** price   **e** cost

58 (elevate, lift)   (improve, enhance)   (1)

    a hike   **b** scale   **c** ascend   **d** raise   **e** empower

59 (law, regulation)   (reign, govern)   (1)

    a power   **b** rule   **c** punish   **d** judge   **e** right

Balance the equation

The two sides of each equation are equal in value. Work out the calculation on the left to find the missing number on the right. Follow the example to answer the questions, then mark the answers on the answer sheet.

60 $12 + 6 = 27 - [\,?\,]$ (1)

    a 11   **b** 8   **c** 21   **d** 9   **e** 12

61 $13 + 5 - 2 = 12 + 7 - [\,?\,]$ (1)

    a 5   **b** 8   **c** 4   **d** 2   **e** 3

62 $8 \times 3 - 5 = 33 \div 3 + [\,?\,]$ (1)

    a 7   **b** 8   **c** 16   **d** 10   **e** 6

63 $48 \div 4 \times 9 = 60 \times 2 - [\,?\,]$ (1)

   a 14   b 16   c 28   d 12   e 2

64 $56 \div 7 \times 6 = 100 \div 4 + [\,?\,]$ (1)

   a 22   b 23   c 27   d 48   e 25

65 $13 \times 7 - 13 = 11 \times 6 + [\,?\,]$ (1)

   a 18   b 24   c 12   d 14   e 8

66 $23 \times 5 - 13 = 10 \times 12 - [\,?\,]$ (1)

   a 21   b 18   c 12   d 13   e 24

Match the number code

These words can be written as number codes and three of the codes are given below. The words and codes are not in the same order.

PORT   TRAP   TART   LENT

     2854   3164   4764

To crack the code, you need to work out which number stands for which letter. Start by looking at numbers that appear more than once. For example, the number 4 appears in three number codes. Then look at the position of the numbers – 4 comes at the end of three codes. Only the letter T can be found at the end of three words. Therefore, the number 4 must represent the letter T.

Work out which word each number code represents to answer the questions, then mark the answers on the answer sheet.

67 Find the code for the word TART. (1)

   a 4383   b 2854   c 2457   d 3691   e 4764

68 Find the word that has the number code 4673. (1)

   a PORT   b TRAP   c PART   d TALL   e TEAR

69 Find the code for the word LENT. (1)

   a 2745   b 3637   c 2854   d 2613   e 5841

These words can be written as number codes and three of the codes are given below. The words and codes are not in the same order.

MATE   DAME   DART   MEAD

     6472   6435   3546

Crack this new code in the same way that you did for the code above.

Work out which word each number code represents to answer the questions, then mark the answers on the answer sheet.

70 Find the code for the word DART. (1)

   a 6274   b 6472   c 4762   d 3645   e 6243

71 Find the word that has the number code 74256. (1)

   a TRADE   b MEANT   c DREAD   d RATED   e TREAD

72 Find the code for the word DREAMT. (1)

   a 347362   b 675432   c 676548   d 274523   e 746352

Statements and questions

Read the following statements and then answer the question that follows.

Archie, Mia, Grace, Will and Molly are cousins.

Mia is two years younger than Grace and one year older than Archie.

Will is a year older than Mia. Molly is a year younger than Grace.

73 Which two cousins are the same age? Mark the answer on the answer sheet. (1)

 a Archie and Mia
 b Mia and Will
 c Will and Molly
 d Grace and Archie
 e Molly and Mia

Letter sequences

Find the missing pair of letters to complete the sequence. Use the alphabet to help you. Follow the example to answer the questions, then mark the answers on the answer sheet.

A B C D E F G H I J K L M N O P Q R S T U V W X Y Z

> **Example**
>
> CE FF IG LH OI [??]
>
> **a** SH   **b** RJ   **c** RK   **d** QJ   **e** QK
>
> Answer: **b** RJ
>
> Count *ahead* three places for the first letter in the pair; count *ahead* one place for the second letter in the pair.

74 AB DE GH JK MN [??] (1)
 a OP   b QR c PP   d PQ e ST

75 DE EG FI GK HM [??] (1)
 a IK   b JL c IO   d IN e MP

76 AB CE EH GK IN [??] (1)
 a JN   b LP c KQ   d MR e OR

77 TS VR YQ CP HO NN   [??] (1)
 a UM   b VL c WK   d TJ e UK

78 BZ YX UV PT JR CP   [??] (1)
 a JM   b IQ c IN   d UN e JS

79 AY EW BU FS CQ GO   [??] (1)
 a BN   b DM c CO   d DP e CR

80 AZ CY GW MT UP EK   [??] (1)
 a BY   b WW c XT   d QE e FY

 Paper 2

Test time: 60 minutes

Download and print the answer sheet from galorepark.co.uk/answersheets before you start this paper.

Antonyms

Find two words, one from each set of brackets, that are *opposite* in meaning. Follow the example to answer the questions then mark the answers on the answer sheet.

> **Example**
>
> (**a** strong   **b** force   **c** afraid)   (**x** fear   **y** weak   **z** test)
>
> Answer: **a** strong, **y** weak
>
> 'Weak' is the opposite of 'strong'. Note that 'afraid' and 'fear' are synonyms (words with similar meanings), not antonyms (opposites).

1 (a fresh   b asleep   c night)   (x dream   y hour   z awake)   (1)
2 (a lead   b path   c chief)   (x group   y follow   z ask)   (1)
3 (a compound   b complex   c tiny)   (x simple   y difficult   z plain)   (1)
4 (a elevate   b descent   c climb)   (x assent   y droop   z ascent) (1)
5 (a diminish   b demolish   c develop)   (x continue   y increase   z discover) (1)
6 (a collect   b captivate   c instil)   (x release   y abandon   z bore)   (1)
7 (a paltry   b pale   c weak)   (x improve   y significant z measure) (1)

Join the words

Make a new word, spelt correctly, by combining two words, one from each group. The word from the left always comes first and there is no change in letter order. Follow the example to answer the questions, then mark the answers on the answer sheet.

8	a	foot	x	lace	(1)
	b	shoe	y	less	
	c	low	z	form	

9	a	wide	x	how	(1)
	b	hid	y	lot	
	c	red	z	den	

10	a	part	x	her	(1)
	b	oar	y	let	
	c	scar	z	man	

11	a	gall	x	ant	(1)
	b	bell	b	age	
	c	miss	z	tie	

12	a	bit	x	let	(1)
	b	wit	y	ham	
	c	bar	z	her	

13	a	bolt	x	age	(1)
	b	gad	y	get	
	c	load	z	gone	

14	a	stall	x	ion	(1)
	b	bold	y	air	
	c	ass	z	robe	

Complete the sentence

Three letters have been removed from the word in capital letters. If they are kept in the same order, these three letters spell another word. Follow the example to answer the questions, then mark the answers on the answer sheet.

15 We posted the TER.   (1)
   a TIN   b RAT   c LET   d WIN   e MAN

16 We have a long break from school in the MER.   (1)
   a SON   b RUB   c BAN   d SUN   e SUM

17 I would RAR eat apples than pears.   (1)
   a THE   b SHE   c BEE   d ATE   e ROT

18 I put the pile of clean TLS on the shelf.   (1)
   a AIR   b OWE   c OAK   d BAR   e EGG

19 SHRS are forecast.   (1)
   a TOR   b ARE   c CAR   d OWE   e OAR

20 My coat got caught on a TTLE.   (1)
   a ATE   b ORE   c EAT   d HIS   e WIN

21 The town was full of TISTS.   (1)
   a ORE   b AIL   c OUR   d EAR   e ARE

Find a common letter

Find *one* letter that will complete the first word and begin the second word in both pairs. The same letter must be added to *both* sets of brackets. Follow the example to answer the questions, then mark the answers on the answer sheet.

> Example
>
> ho [?] op   pa [?] ame
>
> **a** p   **b** d   **c** t   **d** g   **e** n
>
> Answer: **c** t
>
> ho [t] op   pa [t] ame
>
> By adding the letter 't' to both sets of brackets, you make four news words: **hot, top, pat, tame.**

22 ha [?] ap   ar [?] ip   (1)
   a d   b e   c m   d t   e y

23 bea [?] ame   loa [?] irt   (1)
   a f   b t   c n   d r   e d

24 lim [?] arn   we [?] oat   (1)
   a e   b p   c k   d b   e d

25 pal [?] ink   woo [?] ate   (1)
   a e   b l   c m   d d   e w

26 see [?] ove   rea [?] ave   (1)
   a d   b m   c n   d l   e r

27 plan [?] eel   stal [?] een   (1)
   a s   b t   c k   d l   e n

28 plum [?] ager   dol [?] erie   (1)
   a p   b w   c b   d e   e y

Deductions

Read the statements and then answer the question that follows.

> Claire lives due north of her school.
>
> Her house is north west of the sports centre.
>
> Due north of the sports centre is the park.
>
> These four places form the points of a square.

29 Where is the park in relation to Claire's school? Mark the answer on the
   answer sheet.   (1)

   a   south east   b   west   c   east   d   north east   e   north

Letter analogies

Find what links the pairs of letters in the pattern below. Then, using the same pattern, write
the two letters that complete the second pair. Use the alphabet to help you. Follow the
example to answer the questions, then mark the answers on the answer sheet.

A B C D E F G H I J K L M N O P Q R S T U V W X Y Z

> **Example**
>
> **DW** is to **EV** as **JQ** is to [??]
>
> a LM   b KM   c KL   d KP   e LP
>
> Answer: **d** KP
>
> Count *ahead* one place for the first letter in the pair; count *back* one place for the
> second letter in the pair.

30 **HI** is to **JM** as **NO** is to [??]   (1)

   a   PT   b   QU   c   QT   d   PS   e   PT

31 **CE** is to **FI** as **FH** is to [??]   (1)

   a   IL   b   KM   c   JL   d   IK   e   MP

32 **BF** is to **DE** as **PU** is to [??]   (1)

   a   RV   b   RT   c   WR   d   SQ   e   SW

33 **GF** is to **KD** as **NM** is to [??]   (1)

   a   RL   b   QN   c   RK   d   SK   e   RJ

34 **NQ** is to **IW** as **QT** is to [??]   (1)

   a   MT   b   OR   c   KY   d   LZ   e   MY

35 **AD** is to **JX** as **KN** is to [??]   (1)

   a   NP   b   HM   c   TH   d   QE   e   SJ

36 **PT** is to **CA** as **NR** is to [??]   (1)

   a   BZ   b   AY   c   XC   d   BV   e   AZ

Word analogies

Find *one* word in *each* set of brackets to complete the sentence in the most sensible way. Follow the example to answer the questions, then mark the answers on the answer sheet.

> **Example**
>
> **Cap** is to (lid   hat   head) as **sock** is to (shoe   foot   wool).
>
> **a** lid   **b** hat   **c** head   **x** shoe   **y** foot   **z** wool
>
> Answer: **c** head, **y** foot   [**Cap** is to **head** as **sock** is to **foot**.]
>
> You put a <u>cap</u> on your <u>head</u> and a <u>sock</u> on your <u>foot</u>.

37 Water is to (cold   wet   ice) as dust is to (desert   air   dry).   (1)
   a cold   **b** wet   **c** ice   **x** desert   **y** air   **z** dry

38 Hour is to (minute   late   time) as metre is to (ruler   length   measure).   (1)
   a minute   **b** late   **c** time   **x** ruler   **y** length   **z** measure

39 Elbow is to (hand   arm   shoulder) as knee is to (leg   thigh   toe).   (1)
   a hand   **b** arm   **c** shoulder   **x** leg   **y** thigh   **z** toe

40 Earth is to (globe   planet   home) as Sun is to (space   heat   star).   (1)
   a globe   **b** planet   **c** home   **x** space   **y** heat   **z** star

41 Product is to (item   collect   multiply) as sum is to (total   add   few).   (1)
   a item   **b** collect   **c** multiply   **x** total   **y** add   **z** few

42 Seven is to (eight   odd   prime) as sixteen is to (square   four   divide).   (1)
   a eight   **b** odd   **c** prime   **x** square   **y** four   **z** divide

Find the hidden word

Find a word, made up of four letters, that crosses two other words. Follow the example to answer the questions, then mark the answers on the answer sheet.

> **Example**
>
> Hannah tipped the contents of her purse all around the desk.
>
> **a** Hannah tipped   **b** tipped the   **c** her purse   **d** purse all   **e** the desk
>
> Answer: **d** purse all   [seal]
>
> Hannah tipped the contents of her pur<u>se all</u> around the desk.

43 The door burst open and the teacher came in.   (1)
   a   The door   **b**   door burst   **c**   burst open   **d**   and the   **e**   teacher came

44 They store all their camping gear in our loft.   (1)
   a   They store **b**   store all   **c**   all their   **d**   camping gear   **e**   our loft

45 Dad made the arrangements for our holiday to the seaside.   (1)
   a   Dad made   **b**   made the   **c**   the arrangements **d**   for our   **e**   the seaside

46 My brother was ill but he feels much better today.   (1)
   a   my brother **b**   was ill   **c**   feels much   **d**   much better   **e**   better today

47 The frog returned to the same pond every spring.   (1)
   a   The frog   **b**   frog returned **c**   same pond   **d**   pond every   **e**   every spring

48 Gina made her own way to the school picnic.   (1)
   a   Gina made   **b**   made her   **c**   her own   **d**   own way   **e**   school picnic

49 This town is full of wonderful things to see and do.   (1)
   a   This town   **b**   town is   **c**   full of   **d**   wonderful things **e**   see and

Spot the difference

Identify the *two* words that do not belong with the other three in these sets of words. Follow the example to answer the questions, then mark the answers on the answer sheet.

50	a	football	b	tennis	c	racquet	d	hockey	e	bat	(1)
51	a	oak	b	maple	c	acorn	d	sycamore	e	conker	(1)
52	a	thicket	b	glade	c	copse	d	clearing	e	spinney	(1)
53	a	interrupt	b	contribute	c	disturb	d	intrude	e	converse	(1)
54	a	apply	b	opening	c	position	d	exert	e	vacancy	(1)
55	a	wing	b	dependant	c	charge	d	hospital	e	ward	(1)
56	a	treat	b	cake	c	cure	d	prize	e	heal	(1)
57	a	assume	b	verify	c	presume	d	believe	e	prove	(1)

Statement logic

Read the following statements:

> Eddy, Casper, Amy and Eve are comparing the homework they need to do today.
>
> Eddy and Eve both have maths homework.
>
> Casper is finishing a geography project tonight.
>
> Amy and Eddy both have history homework.
>
> Casper often leaves his homework until the last minute.

58 If the statements above are true, this must mean that only *one* of the following statements can be *true*. Which one? Mark the answer on the answer sheet.   (1)

     a   Casper's geography project is due tomorrow.

     b   Amy is never given maths homework.

     c   Eddy has at least two pieces of homework to complete.

     d   Amy does not like geography.

     e   Eve does not study history at school.

Match the letter changes

From the first two pairs of words, identify how the first word is changed to give the second word. Apply the same change to complete the third pair in the same way. Follow the example to answer the questions, then mark the answers on the answer sheet.

59 meat, team   leek, keel   pool, ...   (1)

    a   mast   b   pale   c   loop   d   pole   e   play

60 first, rift   nurse, rune   paces, ...   (1)

    a   space   b   spare   c   species   d   caps   e   cape

61 slate, tale   brace, care   stone, ...   (1)

    a   tone   b   some   c   tons   d   nose   e   note

62 parcel, race   morsel, rose   listen, ...   (1)

    a   late   b   lost   c   lite   d   site   e   line

63 suggest, guest   blender, elder   plaster, ...   (1)

    a   plate   b   alter   c   slate   d   rates   e   later

64 garage, gear   karate, tear   deride, ...   (1)

    a   dear   b   deer   c   ride   d   died   e   deed

65 rooster, store   plaster, stare   whisper, ...   (1)

    a   spare   b   wasps   c   spear   d   spire   e   sphere

Basic algebra

In this sum, letters stand for numbers. Work out the sum and match the answer to the correct code letter. Follow the example to answer the questions, then mark the answers on the answer sheet.

> **Example**
>
> $A = 2$ $B = 3$ $C = 5$ $D = 6$ $E = 1$ $A \times B - E = [?]$
>
> **a**   A   **b**   B   **c**   C   **d**   D   **e**   E
>
> Answer: **c** C
>
> $2 \times 3 - 1 = 5$

66 $A = 3$ $B = 4$ $C = 5$ $D = 6$ $E = 8$ $A + C - B = [?]$ (1)

    a   A   b   B   c   C   d   D   e   E

67 $A = 2$ $B = 3$ $C = 8$ $D = 9$ $E = 12$ $E \div A \times B - D = [?]$ (1)

    a   A   b   B   c   C   d   D   e   E

68 $A = 3$ $B = 10$ $C = 11$ $D = 13$ $E = 28$ $B \times A + C - E = [?]$ (1)

    a   A   b   B   c   C   d   D   e   E

69 $A = 2$ $B = 4$ $C = 5$ $D = 7$ $E = 19$ $B \div A \times D + C = [?]$ (1)

    a   A   b   B   c   C   d   D   e   E

70 $A = 3$ $B = 12$ $C = 20$ $D = 23$ $E = 24$ $E \div A + B + A = [?]$ (1)

    a   A   b   B   c   C   d   D   e   E

71 $A = 2$ $B = 3$ $C = 4$ $D = 14$ $E = 16$ $E \div A \times B + C - D = [?]$ (1)

    a   A   b   B   c   C   d   D   e   E

72 $A = 8$ $B = 10$ $C = 12$ $D = 22$ $E = 36$ $E \div C \times A + B - D = [?]$ (1)

    a   A   b   B   c   C   d   D   e   E

Number analogies

The three numbers in each set of brackets in each question are all related in the same way. Work out how they are related, from the first two brackets, then apply the same pattern to complete the third set. Follow the example to answer the questions, then mark the answers on the answer sheet.

Example

(3 [21] 7)   (5 [20] 4)   (4 [?] 6)

a 4   b 6   c 10   d 24   e 22

Answer: **d** 24

The rule is: multiply the outer numbers to give the middle number.

$3 \times 7 = 21$ $5 \times 4 = 20$ $4 \times 6 = \mathbf{24}$

73 (2 [8] 4)   (3 [12] 4)   (7 [?] 3)   (1)

    a 10   b 12   c 24   d 21   e 35

74 (3 [7] 2)   (5 [21] 4)   (7 [?] 8)   (1)

    a 15   b 16   c 57   d 23   e 22

75 (3 [23] 9)   (5 [31] 7)   (6 [?] 6)   (1)

    a 32   b 8   c 36   d 18   e 16

76 (9 [69] 7)   (6 [30] 4)   (5 [?] 9)   (1)

    a 54   b 51   c 20   d 10   e 48

77 (12 [8] 2)   (15 [5] 5)   (24 [?] 3)   (1)

    a 29   b 27   c 8   d 10   e 12

78 (25 [3] 5)   (10 [0] 5)   (16 [?] 2)   (1)

    a 8   b 16   c 6   d 0   e 12

79 (2 [8] 2)   (3 [27] 3)   (5 [?] 5)   (1)

    a 150   b 125   c 25   d 20   e 115

80 (5 [12] 3)   (6 [25] 5)   (3 [?] 7)   (1)

    a 14   b 10   c 17   d 3   e 13

Paper 3

Download and print the answer sheet from galorepark.co.uk/answersheets before you start this paper.

Move a single letter

Make two new words by moving one letter from the first word and adding it to the second, without moving any other letters. Follow the example to answer the questions, then mark the answers on the answer sheet.

> ### Example
>
> crave   pea
>
> **a** c   **b** r   **c** a   **d** v   **e** e
>
> Answer: **b** r [cave, pear]
>
> Moving the r in 'crave' to the end of 'pea' makes the two new words: 'cave' is a hollow in a rock, 'pear' is a kind of fruit.

1 boast   book   (1)
    a b   b o   c a   d s   e t

2 plain   star   (1)
    a p   b l   c a   d i   e n

3 focal   hair   (1)
    a f   b o   c c   d a   e l

4 glass   ban   (1)
    a g   b l   c a   d s   e s

5 float   pet   (1)
    a f   b l   c o   d a   e t

6 bleak   mode   (1)
    a b   b l   c e   d a   e k

7 shore   bead   (1)
    a s   b h   c o   d r   e e

Number sequences

Find the number from the options that completes each number sequence in the most sensible way. Follow the example to answer the questions, then mark the answers on the answer sheet.

> **Example**
> 7, 14, 21, 28, 35, [?]
> **a** 42   **b** 36   **c** 49   **d** 70   **e** 56
> Answer: **a** 42
> The sequence adds 7 more to every number.

8   6, 12, 18, 24, 30, [?]   (1)

    a   34   b   36   c   38   d   24   e   38

9   4, 7, 6, 9, 8, [?]   (1)

    a   11   b   13   c   16   d   9   e   12

10 28, 24, 20, 16, 12, [?]   (1)

    a   10   b   6   c   8   d   9   e   4

11 13, 11, 7, 5, 3, [?]   (1)

    a   4   b   6   c   2   d   1   e   0

12 5, 10, 6, 11, 7, [?]   (1)

    a   10   b   13   c   12   d   15   e   17

13 2, 4, 3, 9, 8, [?]   (1)

    a   12   b   16   c   10   d   32   e   64

14 1, 10, 4, 8, 9, 6, [?]   (1)

    a   4   b   12   c   16   d   18   e   22

Find a common letter

Find *one* letter that will complete the first word and begin the second word in both pairs. The same letter must be added to *both* sets of brackets. Follow the example to answer the questions, then mark the answers on the answer sheet.

> ## Example
> ho [?] op   pa [?] ame
>
> **a** p   **b** d   **c** t   **d** g   **e** n
>
> Answer: **c t**
>
> ho [t] op   pa [t] ame
>
> By adding the letter 't' to both sets of brackets, you make four news words: **hot, top, pat, tame.**

15 hi [?] at   ar [?] ist   (1)

  a t   **b** l   **c** d   **d** s   **e** m

16 fla [?] reat   ran [?] lade   (1)

  a m   **b** t   **c** g   **d** e   **e** p

17 bar [?] ear   glea [?] ose   (1)

  a k   **b** n   **c** t   **d** r   **e** b

18 brai [?] ote   gla [?] ine   (1)

  a n   **b** l   **c** t   **d** m   **e** d

19 poo [?] ain   spea [?] ing   (1)

  a l   **b** t   **c** r   **d** m   **e** n

20 grow [?] eap   grai [?] acy   (1)

  a n   **b** d   **c** s   **d** l   **e** m

21 flou [?] out   blea [?] aft   (1)

  a n   **b** p   **c** r   **d** t   **e** b

Statement logic

Read the following statements:

> Hattie, Eve, Marcus and Rohan complete a survey about how they get to school.
>
> Eve and Rohan both catch the number 10 bus.
>
> Marcus usually walks to school but gets a lift if it is raining.
>
> Hattie gets a lift every day because her father works near the school.
>
> Marcus and Rohan live in the same street.
>
> Rohan lives nearer the school than Hattie.

22 If the statements above are true, this must mean that only *one* of the following statements can be *true*. Which one? Mark your answer on the answer sheet.   (1)

  a   Hattie lives further from the school than Eve.

  b   Nobody in Rohan's family drives a car.

  c   If it is sunny, Marcus walks to school.

  d   The children all get to school in different ways.

  e   Hattie lives too far from the school to walk.

Match the meaning

Choose *one* word from the list that has a link with the words in both sets of brackets. Follow the example to answer the questions, then mark the answers on the answer sheet.

23 (circle, band)   (chime, toll)   (1)

   a   bell   b   ring   c   round   d   instrument   e   music

24 (make, produce)   (document, sheet)   (1)

   a   design   b   apply   c   line   d   form   e   record

25 (rescue, protect)   (reserve, keep)   (1)

   a   heal   b   collect   c   hold   d   save   e   hide

26 (coins, money)   (alter, transform)   (1)

   a   buy   b   bank   c   improve   d   raise   e   change

27 (breeze, gust)   (coil, curl)   (1)

   a   breathe   b   roll   c   meander   d   scatter   e   wind

28 (throw, cast)   (ground, stadium)   (1)

   a   play   b   goal   c   pitch   d   ball   e   field

29 (symbol, sign)   (grade, rating)   (1)

   a   score   b   write   c   number   d   mark   e   test

Join the words

Make a new word, spelt correctly, by combining two words, one from each group. The word from the left always comes first and there is no change in letter order. Follow the example to answer the questions, then mark the answers on the answer sheet.

30	a	one	x	way	(1)
	b	to	y	for	
	c	bad	z	day	

31	a	bar	x	and	(1)
	b	pit	y	rage	
	c	page	z	stem	

32	a	for	x	pot	(1)
	b	war	y	den	
	c	lent	z	let	

33	a	to	x	pet	(1)
	b	tar	y	kit	
	c	for	z	ken	

34	a	call	x	bit	(1)
	b	or	y	link	
	c	bar	z	den	

35	a	west	x	her	(1)
	b	rat	y	tor	
	c	bet	z	ten	

36	a	man	x	rein	(1)
	b	for	y	rate	
	c	be	z	rage	

37	a	elm	x	ate	(1)
	b	leg	y	pit	
	c	loss	z	end	

Deduction

Read the statements and then answer the question that follows.

Beth, Amy, Carl, Mario and Lee all love animals.

Beth has never owned a dog.

Beth and Amy each have a cat.

Carl has a hamster.

All the children have a goldfish except Mario.

Mario has a rabbit.

Four of the children each have a dog.

All the children have a hamster each.

38 Who has the most number of pets? Mark the answer on the answer sheet. (1)

    a Beth   b Amy   c Carl   d Mario   e Lee

Letter sequences

Find the missing pair of letters to complete the sequence. Use the alphabet to help you. Follow the example to answer the questions, then mark the answers on the answer sheet.

A B C D E F G H I J K L M N O P Q R S T U V W X Y Z

39 AC   CD   EE   GF   [??]   (1)

   a EF   **b** FH   **c** DE   **d** IG   **e** GI

40 AB   CD   FF   JH   OJ   [??]   (1)

   a QR   **b** RU   **c** UL   **d** UN   **e** TL

41 DN   FM   HL   JK   LJ   [??]   (1)

   a NH   **b** MJ   **c** NI   **d** RH   **e** QI

42 PA   QB   SD   VG   ZK   [??]   (1)

   a EG   **b** XZ   **c** FO   **d** EP   **e** DP

43 NQ   LP   JN   HK   FG   [??]   (1)

   a DB   **b** EC   **c** DF   **d** IH   **e** MI

44 JW   DY   YA   UC   RE   PG   [??]   (1)

   a QK   **b** PJ   **c** OI   **d** TB   **e** RD

45 BC   EZ   DV   GQ   FK   ID   [??]   (1)

   a MW   **b** LV   **c** OV   **d** FL   **e** HV

Word relationships

The middle word in the first triplet has been made from letters taken from the other two words in the triplet. Identify which letters were used to make it and apply the same pattern to complete the second triplet. The answer must be a proper word. Follow the example to answer the questions, then mark the answers on the answer sheet.

46 talk (fare) fire   mine (...) lame   (1)

     a   mile   b   male   c   mane   d   lime   e   meal

47 plan (palm) mean   trip (...) noon   (1)

     a   port   b   pint   c   trio   d   torn   e   poor

48 fare (raid) ride   gate (...) mint   (1)

     a   game   b   main   c   meat   d   team   e   mine

49 here (hurt) shut   norm (...) that   (1)

     a   tart   b   moat   c   hart   d   moth   e   than

50 plant (pack) clock   brows (...) crawl   (1)

     a   crow   b   rows   c   owls   d   robs   e   bowl

51 smile (mist) storm   lions (...) heath   (1)

     a   seat   b   hole   c   seal   d   tile   e   lost

52 create (care) space   ladder (...) wreck   (1)

     a   lead   b   weed   c   read   d   leak   e   kale

Word analogies

Find *one* word in *each* set of brackets to complete the sentence in the most sensible way. Follow the example to answer the questions, then mark the answers on the answer sheet.

> ## Example
>
> **Cap** is to (lid   hat   head) as **sock** is to (shoe   foot   wool).
>
> **a** lid   **b** hat   **c** head   **x** shoe   **y** foot   **z** wool
>
> Answer: **c** head, **y** foot [**Cap** is to **head** as **sock** is to **foot**.]
>
> You put a <u>cap</u> on your <u>head</u> and a <u>sock</u> on your <u>foot</u>.

53 See is to (light   eye   look) as hear is to (ear   sound   loud).   (1)

     a   light   b   eye   c   look   x   ear   y   sound   z   loud

54 Hedge is to (clip   border   plant) as wall is to (tall   brick   builder).   (1)

     a   clip   b   border   c   plant   x   tall   y   brick   z   builder

55 Airport is to (holiday   flight   plane) as station is to (journey   train   rails).   (1)

     a   holiday   b   flight   c   plane   x   journey   y   train   z   rails

56 Scale is to (weigh   fish   skin) as feather is to (wing   bird   soft).   (1)

     a   weigh   b   fish   c   skin   x   wing   y   bird   z   soft

57 Cheese is to (milk   cow   dairy) as bread is to (flour   roll   bake).   (1)

     a   milk   b   cow   c   dairy   x   flour   y   roll   z   bake

58 Wither is to (wrinkle   waste   age) as flourish is to (wave   grow   flair).   (1)

     a   wrinkle   b   waste   c   age   x   wave   y   grow   z   flair

59 Novel is to (fiction   innovative   recent) as common is to (plain   familiar   unoriginal).   (1)

     a   fiction   b   innovative   c   recent   x   plain   y   familiar   z   unoriginal

Balance the equation

The two sides of each equation are equal in value. Work out the calculation on the left in order to find the missing number on the right. Follow the example to answer the questions, then mark the answers on the answer sheet.

Example

$15 - 3 + 5 = 11 + [\,?\,] - 2$

a 5　　　　b 8　　　　c 6　　　　d 4　　　　e 7

Answer: **b** 8 $[15 - 3 + 5 = 11 + \mathbf{8} - 2]$

The calculation on the left $(15 - 3 + 5)$ makes 17 so the calculation on the right $(11 + [\,?\,] - 2)$ must also equal 17. The missing value $[\,?\,]$ must, therefore, be 8 because $11 + 8 - 2 = 19 - 2 = 17$.

60　$30 + 6 - 11 = 16 + 13 - [\,?\,]$　　　　　　　　　　　　　　(1)

　　a 8　　b 7　　c 4　　d 6　　e 11

61　$8 \times 3 + 5 - 2 = 5 \times 5 + [\,?\,]$　　　　　　　　　　　　(1)

　　a 7　　b 2　　c 5　　d 8　　e 3

62　$48 \div 12 \times 7 - 1 = 9 \times 3 - [\,?\,]$　　　　　　　　　　(1)

　　a 4　　b 6　　c 0　　d 9　　e 2

63　$72 \div 8 \times 5 - 22 = 6 \times 3 + [\,?\,]$　　　　　　　　　　(1)

　　a 8　　b 5　　c 8　　d 12　　e 3

64　$99 \div 9 \times 4 + 4 = 12 \times 3 + [\,?\,]$　　　　　　　　　　(1)

　　a 7　　b 12　　c 11　　d 15　　e 3

65　$26 \div 2 \times 4 - 14 = 14 \times 5 + 2 - [\,?\,]$　　　　　　　(1)

　　a 38　　b 24　　c 34　　d 15　　e 44

66　$39 \div 3 \times 2 + 16 = 13 \times 4 - [\,?\,]$　　　　　　　　　(1)

　　a 14　　b 12　　c 20　　d 10　　e 17

Apply the code

In each question a given word is written in code. Work out the code and apply it to encode the second word. The alphabet has been provided to help you. Follow the example to answer the questions, then mark the answers on the answer sheet.

A B C D E F G H I J K L M N O P Q R S T U V W X Y Z

> **Example**
>
> If the code for READ is PCYB, what is the code for SENT?
>
> **a** TFOU   **b** CQLR   **c** RFMS   **d** QCLR   **e** RBKQ
>
> Answer: **d** QCLR
>
> Count *back* two places from each letter in the given word to find the corresponding code letter.

67 If the code for BEAR is EHDU, what is the code for PINE? (1)

     a ZMHC   b SNJB   c SLQH   d TNLC   e YMGX

68 If the code for WRAP is OJSH, what is the code for DIVE? (1)

     a KPZE   b YTOJ   c VANW   d NAVI   e GNJA

69 If the code for BRAN is CTBP, what is the word for IQQG? (1)

     a PART   b RAIN   c HOPE   d SOAP   e RATE

70 If the code for VEST is CLZA, what is the word for AYHF? (1)

     a HARP   b TRAY   c PORT   d SLIP   e CARE

71 If the code for CLEAR is DNHEW, what is the code for TRICK? (1)

     a MXIDJ   b OUXDE   c UTLGP   d QOGAI   e SLJYB

72 If the code for BOARD is YLZIW, what is the code for TRUTH? (1)

     a ROIRD   b FGJFU   c RIFRS   d GLQTB   e GIFGS

73 If the code for PLAIN is QOFPW, what is the word for EUNUT? (1)

     a BRING   b DRINK   c MONEY   d STORE   e BLAME

Match the number code

These words can be written as number codes and three of the codes are given below. The words and codes are not in the same order.

LEAP   PACE   PEAR   PILE

    4712   1234   4236

To crack the code, you need to work out which number stands for which letter. Start by looking at numbers that appear more than once. For example, the number 4 appears in three number codes. Then look at the position of the numbers – 4 comes at the start of two codes and at the end of one code. Only the letter P can be found at the start and end of a word. Therefore, the number 4 must represent the letter P.

Work out which word each number code represents to answer these questions, then mark the answers on the answer sheet.

74 Find the code for the word PEAR. (1)

    a 4712   b 7421   c 1234   d 4763   e 4236

75 Find the code for the word PILE. (1)

    a 5127   b 4712   c 4326   d 1467   e 2416

76 Find the word that has the number code 4352. (1)

    a REAP   b ROLE   c PACE   d LEAP   e PALE

These words can be written as number codes and three of the codes are given below. The words and codes are not in the same order.

TERM   MORE   MOAT   TAME

    6954   8456   6978

Crack this new code in the same way that you did for the code above. Work out which word each number code represents to answer the questions, then mark the answers on the answer sheet.

77 Find the word that has the number code 6954. (1)

    a TERM   b MOAT   c MORE   d TAME   e MATE

78 Find the word that has the code 8758. (1)

    a TAME   b TART   c RARE   d ROAR   e TOOT

79 Find the code for the word MOTOR. (1)

    a 69598   b 68786   c 49895   d 54846   e 69895

Statement logic

Read the following statements:

Zoe, Marcus, Anika, Tia and Chris take part in a sponsored silence to raise money for charity.

They all begin at ten o'clock in the morning.

Marcus speaks after ninety minutes.

Zoe ends her silence at noon.

Chris is silent for twice as long as Marcus.

Tia starts speaking fifteen minutes after Marcus.

Anika is silent for less time than Zoe.

80 If the statements above are true, this must mean that only *one* of the following statements can be *true*. Which one? Mark the answer on the answer sheet. (1)

 a Zoe raises the most money for charity.
 b Zoe and Marcus speak at the same time.
 c Anika finds it the most difficult to remain silent.
 d Chris is silent for one hour longer than Zoe.
 e Tia is silent for the longest time.

 # Paper 4

Download and print the answer sheet from galorepark.co.uk/answersheets before you start this paper.

Join the words

Make a new word, spelt correctly, by combining two words, one from each group. The word from the left always comes first and there is no change in letter order. Follow the example to answer the questions, then mark the answers on the answer sheet.

> **Example**
>
> **a** cab **x** over
> **b** man **y** in
> **c** call **z** end
> Answer: **a** cab, **y** in [cabin]
> 'cab'+ 'in' makes the word 'cabin' (a log hut).

1 a know   x let   (1)
   b care   y hole
   c leaf   z ring

2 a bar   x kit   (1)
   b for   y tin
   c ban   z age

3 a was   x ton   (1)
   b lot   y her
   c will   z low

4 a war   x vex   (1)
   b ice   y flow
   c con   z fall

5 a heat   x in   (1)
   b let   y char
   c par   z her

6 a will   x ten   (1)
   b base   y den
   c has   z cue

7 a amp   x pole   (1)
   b on   y ion
   c man   z let

8 a reap   x pore   (1)
   b tor   y bond
   c mind   z ply

Word analogies

Find *one* word in *each* set of brackets to complete the sentence in the most sensible way. Follow the example to answer the questions, then mark the answers on the answer sheet.

> **Example**
> **Cap** is to (lid   hat   head) as **sock** is to (shoe   foot   wool).
> **a** lid   **b** hat   **c** head   **x** shoe   **y** foot   **z** wool
> Answer: **c** head, **y** foot [**Cap** is to **head** as **sock** is to **foot**.]
> You put a <u>cap</u> on your <u>head</u> and a <u>sock</u> on your <u>foot</u>.

9 Kitten is to (fur   cat   claws) as puppy is to (small   tail   dog).   (1)
     a fur   b cat   c claws   x small   y tail   z dog

10 Lace is to (bow   frill   shoe) as button is to (hole   shirt   fix).   (1)
     a bow   b frill   c shoe   x hole   y shirt   z fix

11 Club is to (join   golf   member) as stick is to (glue   tree   hockey).   (1)
     a join   b golf   c member   x glue   y tree   z hockey

12 Theatre is to (ticket   play   audience) as cinema is to (actor   scene   film).   (1)
     a ticket   b play   c audience   x actor   y scene   z film

13 Knife is to (fork   sharp   meal) as cup is to (china   tea   saucer).   (1)
     a fork   b sharp   c meal   x china   y tea   z saucer

14 Library is to (shelves   collection   book) as bank is to (save   money   verge).   (1)
     a shelves b collection c book   x save   y money z verge

15 Comb is to (teeth   hair   brush) as brush is to (sweep   bristle   clean).   (1)
     a teeth   b hair   c brush   x sweep   y bristle z clean

Basic algebra

In this sum, letters stand for numbers. Work out the sum and match the answer to the correct code letter. Follow the example to answer the questions, then mark the answers on the answer sheet.

Example

A = 2   B = 3   C = 5   D = 6   E = 1 $A \times B - E = [?]$

a A   b B   c C   d D   e E

Answer: c C

$2 \times 3 - 1 = 5$

16	A = 8	B = 9	C = 2	D = 3	E = 7	$A + D - B = [?]$	(1)
	a A	b B	c C	d D	e E		
17	A = 3	B = 4	C = 6	D = 21	E = 20	$E \div B \times A + C = [?]$	(1)
	a A	b B	c C	d D	e E		
18	A = 5	B = 10	C = 12	D = 35	E = 90	$B \times C + A - D = [?]$	(1)
	a A	b B	c C	d D	e E		
19	A = 3	B = 5	C = 18	D = 24	E = 60	$E \div B \times A - C = [?]$	(1)
	a A	b B	c C	d D	e E		
20	A = 3	B = 24	C =11	D = 99	E = 8	$D \div C \times A + E - C = [?]$	(1)
	a A	b B	c C	d D	e E		
21	A = 0	B = 10	C = 13	D = 18	E = 36	$E \div D \times C + B - A = [?]$	(1)
	a A	b B	c C	d D	e E		
22	A = 4	B = 84	C = 38	D = 29	E = 3	$B \div A \times E + A - D = [?]$	(1)
	a A	b B	c C	d D	e E		

Deduction

Read the following statements and then answer the question that follows.

Five children are planning birthday celebrations this year.

None of the children has a birthday in the first three months of the year.

Mia's birthday falls in a month ending in Y.

Harry's birthday falls in a month with 30 days.

Lottie's birthday is two months before Ruby's.

George's birthday is in the same month as Halloween.

Ruby's birthday falls ten months after the shortest month.

23 Which two children were born in the same month? Mark the answer on the answer sheet. (1)

   a   Mia and Harry
   b   Harry and Ruby
   c   George and Lottie
   d   Ruby and Mia
   e   Lottie and Harry

Letter analogies

Find what links the pairs of letters in the pattern below. Then, using the same pattern, write the two letters that complete the second pair. Use the alphabet to help you. Follow the example to answer the questions, then mark the answers on the answer sheet.

A B C D E F G H I J K L M N O P Q R S T U V W X Y Z

> **Example**
>
> **DW** is to **EV** as **JQ** is to [??]
>
> **a** LM **b** KM **c** KL **d** KP **e** LP
>
> Answer: **d** KP
>
> Count *ahead* one place for the first letter in the pair; count *back* one place for the second letter in the pair.

24 **BE** is to **HK** as **NQ** is to [??] (1)
     a TV   b SW   c WU   d TW   e QT

25 **CT** is to **FS** as **NP** is to [??] (1)
     a LM   b QO   c RO   d QN   e TO

26 **BC** is to **YX** as **EF** is to [??] (1)
     a VU   b QP   c LK   d UV   e WY

27 **CE** is to **HB** as **NP** is to [??] (1)
     a OI   b MJ   c SM   d VS   e XU

28 **BM** is to **VP** as **DZ** is to [??] (1)
     a YB   b JC   c WD   d NT   e XC

29 **HB** is to **JX** as **YC** is to [??] (1)
     a VY   b AY   c DG   d AW   e WA

30 **WB** is to **EW** as **TC** is to [??] (1)
     a DY   b FW   c DV   d BX   e TO

Synonyms and antonyms

Find *two* words, one from each set of brackets, that are *most similar* in meaning. Follow the example to answer the questions, then mark the answers on the answer sheet.

> **Example**
>
> (**a** slip **b** jump **c** leap) (**x** skip **y** slide **z** step)
>
> Answer: **a** slip, **y** slide
>
> Both 'slip' and 'slide' mean to slither – 'jump' and 'leap' are synonyms (words with similar meanings) but in the same set of brackets so cannot be selected.

31 (a close b far c by) (x touch y near z for) (1)
32 (a fire b danger c safe) (x risk y flood z hot) (1)
33 (a chase b flee c free) (x hide y lose z escape) (1)
34 (a shake b mend c flaw) (x decent y defect z affix) (1)
35 (a scale b score c creep) (x fish y fall z climb) (1)
36 (a hero b brave c will) (x conform y afraid z confront) (1)
37 (a bright b attract c ember) (x flare y vivid z blaze) (1)

Moving a single letter

Make *two* new words by moving one letter from the first word and adding it to the second, without moving any other letters. Follow the example to answer the questions, then mark the answers on the answer sheet.

> ### Example
>
> crave   pea
>
> **a**   c   **b**   r   **c**   a   **d**   v   **e**   e
>
> Answer: **b** r [cave, pear]
>
> Moving the r in 'crave' to the end of 'pea' makes the two new words: 'cave' is a hollow in a rock, 'pear' is a kind of fruit.

38 clasp   rat   (1)

    a   c   b   l   c   a   d   s   e   p

39 chief   pan   (1)

    a   c   b   h   c   i   d   e   e   f

40 gloat   mat   (1)

    a   g   b   l   c   o   d   a   e   t

41 claim   alas   (1)

    a   c   b   l   c   a   d   i   e   m

42 pearl   weak   (1)

    a   p   b   e   c   a   d   r   e   l

43 grain   bugle   (1)

    a   g   b   r   c   a   d   i   e   n

44 avoid   repel   (1)

    a   a   b   v   c   o   d   i   e   d

Statement logic

Read the following statements:

> Rajvi has been given five gifts for her birthday.
>
> Gift A has red wrapping paper and a yellow bow.
>
> Gift B has blue wrapping paper.
>
> Gift C and Gift D both have spotty wrapping paper and no bows.
>
> Gift E has both a tag and bow.
>
> All of the gifts except Gift A have a gift tag.
>
> Gift B is wrapped in the same paper as Gift C.
>
> One gift has a birthday card attached.

45 If the statements above are true, this must mean that only *one* of the following statements can be *true*. Which one? Mark the answer on the answer sheet.   (1)

    a   Two gifts have red wrapping paper.

    b   Only gifts with spotty paper have no bows.

    c   Gift E has a yellow bow.

    d   Three gifts have spotty wrapping paper.

    e   Gift A has a birthday card attached.

Apply the code

In each question a given word is written in code. Work out the code and apply it to encode the second word. The alphabet has been provided to help you. Follow the example to answer the questions, then mark the answers on the answer sheet.

A B C D E F G H I J K L M N O P Q R S T U V W X Y Z

> ## Example
>
> If the code for READ is PCYB, what is the code for SENT?
>
> **a** TFOU   **b** CQLR   **c** RFMS   **d** QCLR   **e** RBKQ
>
> Answer: **d** QCLR
>
> Count *back* two places from each letter in the given word to find the corresponding code letter.

46 If the code for BUSH is DWUJ, what is the code for COAT?   (1)

    a   ACRP   b   EQTP   c   EQCV   d   FPCV   e   ERDU

47 If the code for VIEW is BOKC, what is the code for YEAR?   (1)

    a   GDHY   b   ECIZ   c   DLCT   d   EKGX   e   KMXU

48 If the code for BEAR is XAWN, what is the word for RAOP?   (1)

    a   POST   b   VEST   c   RAIN   d   FORT   e   VAIN

49 If the code for SHUT is BQDC, what is the word for AXYN?   (1)

    a   LIST   b   POLE   c   SAIL   d   ROSE   e   ROPE

50 If the code for POOL is QQRP, what is the code for TRAY?   (1)

    a   USCZ   b   VTBX   c   UTDC   d   TTCZ   e   SQVH

51 If the code for WAVE is DZEV, what is the word for WVZI?   (1)

    a   DALE   b   COAL   c   PALE   d   DEBT   e   DEAR

52 If the code for STAR is RRXN, what is the word for LGKP?   (1)

    a   MAST   b   MINT   c   NOSE   d   PINT   e   LINT

Match the number code

These words can be written as number codes and three of the codes are given below. The words and codes are not in the same order.

FAIR   MARE   RARE   FAME

      2326   5326   1342

To crack the code, you need to work out which number stands for which letter. Start by looking at numbers that appear more than once. For example, the number 6 appears at the end of two number codes. Then look at the position of the letters – E comes at the end of three words. Therefore, the number 6 must represent the letter E.

Work out which word each number code represents to answer these questions, then mark the answers on the answer sheet.

53 Find the code for the word RARE.   (1)

    a 1356   b 5326   c 1344   d 2326   e 2356

54 Find the code for the word FAIR.   (1)

    a 5326   b 1342   c 1356   d 1534   e 4561

55 Find the word that has the number code 5326.   (1)

    a FAIR   b FAME   c MARE   d FARM   e FARE

These words can be written as number codes and three of the codes are given below. The words and codes are not in the same order. Work out which word each number code represents to answer these questions, then mark the answers on the answer sheet.

CARE   LACE   COPE   REAP

      1564   1234   7514

56 Find the code for REAP.   (1)

    a 1234   b 3214   c 1564   d 6453   e 6452

57 Find the code for the word PEACE.   (1)

    a 53214   b 34514   c 61545   d 54234   e 35415

58 Find the word that has the number code 356147.   (1)

    a APPLE   b PARCEL   c COUPLE   d PLACER   e RAPPER

Find the hidden word

Find a word, made up of four letters, that crosses two other words. Follow the example to answer the questions, then mark the answers on the answer sheet.

> **Example**
>
> Hannah tipped the contents of her purse all around the desk.
>
> **a** Hannah tipped   **b** tipped the   **c** her purse   **d** purse all   **e** the desk
>
> Answer: **d** purse all [seal]
>
> Hannah tipped the contents of her pur<u>se al</u>l around the desk.

59 There was a raffle at the school fair last April. (1)

   a   There was   b   raffle at   c   school fair   d   fair last   e   last April

60 We saw an ancient stone arch when we visited Rome. (1)

   a   We saw   b   an ancient   c   ancient stone   d   stone arch   e   when we

61 My little brother's sandpit has enough room for all of his friends. (1)

   a   little brother's   b   sandpit has   c   has enough   d   room for   e   his friends

62 We opened the car windows and let in the cool breeze. (1)

   a   opened the   b   car windows   c   windows and   d   the cool   e   cool breeze

63 It would be so funny if Dad fell into the water when we go fishing! (1)

   a   would be   b   so funny   c   fell into   d   the water e   go fishing

64 Any rain tomorrow could ruin our summer picnic at school. (1)

   a   rain tomorrow   b   tomorrow could   c   ruin our

   d   summer picnic   e   at school

65 Our new puppy sometimes sleeps on my bed. (1)

   a   new puppy   b   puppy sometimes   c   sometimes sleeps

   d   sleeps on   e   my bed

Match the letter changes

From the first two pairs of words, identify how the first word is changed to give the second word. Apply the same change to complete the third pair in the same way. Follow the example to answer the questions, then mark the answers on the answer sheet.

> ### Example
> lead, deal   sent, tens   peek, ...
> **a** leek   **b** leak   **c** seek   **d** keep   **e** seal
> Answer: **d** keep
> The first and last letters change place in the second word.

66 cask, cake   mast, mate   talk, ... (1)

   a   late   b   tale   c   kale   d   take   e   task

67 tone, tame   lose, lame   sole, ... (1)

   a   sale   b   same   c   lose   d   seal   e   mole

68 great, gear   store, sort   bread, ... (1)

   a   read   b   bare   c   bear   d   dear   e   dare

69 weave, view   trade, diet   seams, ... (1)

   a   mass   b   same   c   mess   d   miss   e   arms

70 spell, leap   bleat, teal   blind, ... (1)

   a   nail   b   land   c   dial   d   band   e   lion

71 wastes, stew   glared, dreg   pastes, ... (1)

   a   past   b   step   c   east   d   taps   e   pats

72 please, sale   dreamt, mart   tights, ... (1)

   a   tart   b   sits   c   hits   d   this   e   high

Deduction

Read the following statements and then answer the question that follows.

> Susie read ten books as part of a reading challenge.
>
> Archie read three books fewer than Sam.
>
> Sam read the same number of books as Lily.
>
> Charlotte read two books fewer than Susie and one fewer than Sam.

73 How many books did Archie read? Mark the answer on the answer sheet. (1)

    a 7   b 9   c 8   d 6   e 5

Number sequences

Find the number from the options that completes each number sequence in the most sensible way. Follow the example to answer the questions, then mark the answers on the answer sheet.

> **Example**
>
> 7, 14, 21, 28, 35, [?]
>
> a 42   b 36   c 49   d 70   e 56
>
> Answer: **a** 42
>
> The sequence adds 7 more to every number.

74 1, 2, 4, 7, 11, 16, [?] (1)

    a 19   b 24   c 22   d 32   e 20

75 2, 3, 4, 6, 6, 9, 8, [?] (1)

    a 9   b 12   c 11   d 14   e 6

76 52, 48, 44, 40, 36, [?] (1)

    a 34   b 30   c 32   d 28   e 24

77 11, 9, 7, 10, 5, 11, 3, 12, [?] (1)

    a 1   b 0   c 13   d 2   e 5

78 8, 27, 12, 24, 16, 21, 20, [?] (1)

    a 18   b 24   c 21   d 16   e 15

79 84, 45, 72, 54, 60, 63, 48, [?] (1)

    a 36   b 44   c 72   d 24   e 42

80 15, 21, 19, 25, 23, 29, [?] (1)

    a 27   b 19   c 21   d 23   e 17

Answers

All the references in the boxes below refer to the *11+ Verbal Reasoning Study and Revision Guide* (ISBN: 9781471849244) so you know exactly where to find out more about the question and your answer.

PAPER 1

Find a common letter

1	**b**	t	wit trip	fat tour	(1)
2	**e**	l	owl lend	meal lid	(1)
3	**d**	t	lot tan	moat tap	(1)
4	**b**	e	ape ear	flee earn	(1)
5	**d**	p	harp pour	sap post	(1)
6	**c**	t	bat tug	gait tear	(1)
7	**c**	f	half fend	leaf fail	(1)

Find the hidden word

8	**e**	gear	Our new rabbit has very bi**g ear**s.	(1)
9	**c**	then	I looked wi**th en**vy at the cake.	(1)
10	**c**	heap	Dad sliced **the ap**ple carefully into pieces.	(1)
11	**a**	reel	My th**ree l**ittle cousins always look for food.	(1)
12	**b**	veal	Last year I ga**ve al**l my old school books away.	(1)
13	**d**	calm	All the snow was cleared by lo**cal m**en and women.	(1)
14	**b**	blew	The huge ta**ble w**as covered in many delicious foods.	(1)

Synonyms

15	**b** tear, **y** rip	Tear and rip both mean to pull paper or cloth into pieces.	(1)
16	**a** danger, **y** peril	Danger and peril both mean a threat to someone's safety.	(1)
17	**b** howl, **x** shout	Howl and shout are both loud noises a person might make.	(1)
18	**b** conceal, **y** secrete	Conceal and secrete both mean to hide something.	(1)
19	**a** foolish, **y** absurd	Foolish and absurd both mean behaviour that is not sensible. Dangerous cannot be selected as foolish behaviour is not necessarily dangerous.	(1)
20	**b** flaw, **z** fault	Flaw and fault both mean an imperfection in something.	(1)
21	**a** shy, **z** timid	Shy and timid both mean to be nervous and lacking in self-confidence.	(1)
22	**a** frustrated, **y** discouraged	Frustrated and discouraged are both feelings of dissatisfaction.	(1)

Statement logic

23 **b** Lucy prefers the cinema to bowling. We know this because the second sentence says that Lucy likes the cinema best. Some of the other statements could be true, but we do not have enough evidence to prove this. (1)

For more on answering statement logic questions, see page 88.

Word relationships

24 **d** tale (1)

```
b e a k (k e p t) p o r t        r a f t (t a l e) l a k e
1 2 3 4  4 2 5 8  5 6 7 8        1 2 3 4  4 2 5 8  5 6 7 8
```

25 **b** cart (1)

```
f o l k (l o a f) s t a r        t a c k (c a r t) w a r m
1 2 3 4  3 2 7 1  5 6 7 8        1 2 3 4  3 2 7 1  5 6 7 8
```

26 **e** trap (1)

```
s h i p (s p i n) o v e n        t e a r (t r a p) s o u p
1 2 3 4  1 4 3 8  5 6 7 8        1 2 3 4  1 4 3 8  5 6 7 8
```

27 **b** there (1)

```
g h o s t (s t o k e) s p e c k        t e e t h (t h e r e) c l e a r
1 2 3 4 5  4 5 3 10 8  6 7 8 9 10       1 2 3 4 5  4 5 3 10 8  6 7 8 9 10
                 6
```

28 **d** steam (1)

```
b l e a k (b l a c k) c l u n k        s t e e r (s t e a m) a l a r m
1 2 3 4 5  1 2 4 6 5  6 7 8 9 10        1 2 3 4 5  1 2 4 6 10  6 7 8 9 10
                7   10
```

29 b slump (1)

l e a r n (b r e a d) b r i d e   b u m p s (s l u m p) s l o p e
1 2 3 4 5   6 7 2 3 9   6 7 8 9 10   1 2 3 4 5   6 7 2 3 9   6 7 8 9 10
         4 10

30 d stalest (1)

r e a s o n s (r e s t o r e) s k a t e r s   s t u d e n t (s t a l e s t) a n a l y s t
1 2 3 4 5 6 7   1 2 8 11 5 1 2   8 9 10 11 12 13 14   1 2 3 4 5 6 7   1 2 8 11 5 1 2   8 9 10 11 12 13 14
         13 12 4   13 12   13   13
            7
            14

Move a single letter

31 a	s	Moving the letter 's' from space to tin makes the words pace and tins.	(1)
32 b	t	Moving the letter 't' from sting to fee makes the words sing and feet.	(1)
33 a	b	Moving the letter 'b' from block to one makes the words lock and bone.	(1)
34 c	e	Moving the letter 'e' from niece to clan makes the words nice and clean.	(1)
35 d	w	Moving the letter 'w' from brawn to tine makes the words bran and twine.	(1)
36 b	a	Moving the letter 'a' from paint to stem makes the words pint and steam.	(1)
37 a	w	Moving the letter 'w' from women to net makes the words omen and newt.	(1)

Spot the difference

38 b, e **Bright** and **plain** are not the names of colours. (1)

39 b, e **Sock** and **boot** are not parts of the body. (1)

40 b, e **Carrot** and **onion** are not types of fruit. (1)

41 a, d **Soft** and **image** are not senses. (1)

42 b, e **Soil** and **grow** are not parts of a tree. (1)

43 a, e **Night** and **dark** are not things you can find in space. (1)

44 b, d **Demand** and **desire** are verbs relating to wanting something, while the other words relate to owning something. (1)

45 c, e **Sharp** and **astute** are adjectives relating to being intelligent, while the other words relate to being very keen to do a particular thing. (1)

Complete the sentence

46 b	PIT	My baby brother was born in the hos**pit**al.	(1)
47 c	OUR	Our j**our**ney lasted three hours.	(1)
48 d	LIP	I s**lip**ped on the icy path.	(1)
49 c	MEN	We made an agree**men**t.	(1)
50 d	CAP	Our rabbit es**cap**ed.	(1)
51 c	ASK	Dad had a fl**ask** of coffee.	(1)
52 e	OWL	I love b**owl**ing.	(1)

Match the meaning

53 c post 'Post' is a noun that means a pole or stake; it is also a noun that means written letters. (1)

54 b part 'Part' is a noun that means a piece or section of something; it is also a verb that means to divide or separate the parts of something. (1)

55 e pick 'Pick' is a verb that means to select or choose something; it is also a verb that means to gather or harvest a crop. (1)

56 d beat 'Beat' is a verb that means to strike or hit something; it is also a noun that describes rhythm or tempo in music. (1)

57 b dear 'Dear' is an adjective used to describe something or someone that is beloved or treasured; it can also be used to describe something that is expensive to buy. (1)

58 d raise 'Raise' is a verb meaning to lift up; it can also be used to describe improving or enhancing something, e.g. raise reading age. (1)

59 b rule 'Rule' is a noun meaning a law or regulation that must be followed; it is also a verb that means to reign or govern, like a king or queen. (1)

Balance the equation

60 d 9 (1)

       12 + 6 = 27 − _____
       18 = 27 − _____
       27 − 18 = **9**

61 e 3 (1)

$13 + 5 - 2 = 12 + 7 - \underline{}$

$18 - 2 = 12 + 7 - \underline{}$

$16 = 19 - \underline{}$

$19 - 16 = \mathbf{3}$

62 b 8 (1)

$8 \times 3 - 5 = 33 \div 3 + \underline{}$

$24 - 5 = 33 \div 3 + \underline{}$

$19 = 33 \div 3 + \underline{}$

$19 = 11 + \underline{}$

$19 - 11 = \mathbf{8}$

63 d 12 (1)

$48 \div 4 \times 9 = 60 \times 2 - \underline{}$

$12 \times 9 = 60 \times 2 - \underline{}$

$108 = 60 \times 2 - \underline{}$

$108 = 120 - \underline{}$

$120 - 108 = \mathbf{12}$

64 b 23 (1)

$56 \div 7 \times 6 = 100 \div 4 + \underline{}$

$8 \times 6 = 100 \div 4 + \underline{}$

$48 = 100 \div 4 + \underline{}$

$48 = 25 + \underline{}$

$48 - 25 = \mathbf{23}$

65 c 12 (1)

$13 \times 7 - 13 = 11 \times 6 + \underline{}$

$91 - 13 = 11 \times 6 + \underline{}$

$78 = 11 \times 6 + \underline{}$

$78 = 66 + \underline{}$

$78 - 66 = \mathbf{12}$

66 b 18 (1)

$23 \times 5 - 13 = 10 \times 12 - \underline{}$

$115 - 13 = 10 \times 12 - \underline{}$

$102 = 10 \times 12 - \underline{}$

$102 = 120 - \underline{}$

$120 - 102 = \mathbf{18}$

Match the number code

$1 = O, 2 = L, 3 = P, 4 = T, 5 = N, 6 = R, 7 = A, 8 = E$

The word TART begins and ends with T, so the code with the same number at the start and end must be the code for TART. This enables the code letters for T, A and R to be identified in the other words. The word LENT has only one letter in common with the other words, enabling its identification with the code with only one number in common.

67 e 4764 (1)

68 b TRAP (1)

69 c 2854 (1)

$2 = T, 3 = M, 4 = A, 5 = E, 6 = D, 7 = R$

The words DAME, DART and MEAD contain the letter 'D' either at the end or at the start of the word. The code for 'D' must therefore be 6, because 6 is the only number to be found both at the start and at the end of any of the number codes. This enables the letter codes A, T, E, R and M to be identified in the other words.

70 b 6472 (1)

71 d RATED (1)

72 b 675432 (1)

> For more on answering questions that ask you to match the number code, see page 58.

Statements and questions

73 c   Will and Molly

List the names in order of age, starting with Mia because she is mentioned first. Grace is two years older than Mia. Mia is one year older than Archie. Will is one year older than Mia (and therefore one year younger than Grace). Molly is also one year younger than Grace, so Will and Molly are the same age.

Years older or younger	Name
Mia + 2 years	Grace
Will = Mia + 1 year Molly = Grace – 1 year	Will and Molly
	Mia
Mia – 1 year	Archie

Letter sequences

74 d   PQ   Count *forward* three places for both letters in the pair.   (1)
75 c   IO   Count *forward* one place for the first letter in the pair; count *forward* two places for the second letter in the pair.   (1)
76 c   KQ   Count *forward* two places for the first letter in the pair; count *forward* three places for the second letter in the pair.   (1)
77 a   UM   Count *forward* one more place each time for the first letter in the pair (i.e. +2, +3, +4, etc.), crossing the end of the alphabet; count *back* one place for the second letter in the pair.   (1)
78 d   UN   Count *back* one more place each time for the first letter in the pair (i.e. –3, –4, –5, etc.), crossing the start of the alphabet; count *back* two places for the second letter in the pair.   (1)
79 b   DM   Count in an alternating pattern of *forward* four places then *back* three places for the first letter in the pair; count *back* two places for the second letter in the pair.   (1)
80 d   QE   Count *forward* in multiples of two for the first letter in the pair (i.e. +2, +4, +6, etc.); count *back* one more place each time for the second letter in the pair (i.e. – 1, –2, –3).   (1)

> For more on working with letter sequences, see page 70.

PAPER 2

Antonyms

1 **b** asleep, **z** awake   Asleep is the opposite of awake.   (1)
2 **a** lead, **y** follow   Lead is the opposite of follow.   (1)
3 **b** complex, **x** simple   Complex is the opposite of simple. Note that difficult is a synonym (a word with a similar meaning), not an antonym (opposite) of complex.   (1)
4 **b** descent, **z** ascent   Descent is the opposite of ascent.   (1)
5 **a** diminish, **y** increase   Diminish is the opposite of increase.   (1)
6 **b** captivate, **z** bore   Captivate is the opposite of bore.   (1)
7 **a** paltry, **y** significant   Paltry is the opposite of significant.   (1)

> For more on answering questions about antonyms, see page 26.

Join the words

8   **b**   x   shoelace   (1)
9   **b**   z   hidden   (1)
10 **c**   y   scarlet   (1)
11 **a**   x   gallant   (1)
12 **b**   z   wither   (1)
13 **b**   y   gadget   (1)
14 **a**   x   stallion   (1)

> For more on questions that ask you to join words, see page 18.

Complete the sentence

15	c	LET	We posted the **let**ter.	(1)
16	e	SUM	We have a long break from school in the **sum**mer.	(1)
17	a	THE	I would ra**the**r eat apples than pears.	(1)
18	b	OWE	I put the pile of clean t**owe**ls on the shelf.	(1)
19	d	OWE	Sh**owe**rs are forecast.	(1)
20	d	HIS	My coat got caught on a t**his**tle.	(1)
21	c	OUR	The town was full of t**our**ists.	(1)

For more on answering questions that ask you to complete the sentence, see page 36.

Find a common letter

22	d	t	hat tap	art tip	(1)
23	e	d	bead dame	load dirt	(1)
24	d	b	limb barn	web boat	(1)
25	b	l	pall link	wool late	(1)
26	e	r	seer rove	rear rave	(1)
27	c	k	plank keel	stalk keen	(1)
28	d	e	plume eager	dole eerie	(1)

For more on answering questions that ask you to find a common letter, see page 16.

Deductions

29 d   north east   (1)

Begin by drawing a square. Plot the places on each corner of the square, depending on their position to each other. Once you have plotted all of the places on the square, you will be able to see that the park is north east of Claire's school.

For more on answering questions involving deduction, see page 92.

Letter analogies

30	d	PS	Count *forward* two places for the first letter in the pair; count *forward* four places for the second letter in the pair.	(1)
31	a	IL	Count *forward* three places for the first letter in the pair; count *forward* four places for the second letter in the pair.	(1)
32	b	RT	Count *forward* two places for the first letter in the pair; count *back* one place for the second letter in the pair.	(1)
33	c	RK	Count *forward* four places for the first letter in the pair; count *back* two places for the second letter in the pair.	(1)
34	d	LZ	Count *back* five places for the first letter in the pair; count *forward* six places for the second letter in the pair.	(1)
35	c	TH	Count *forward* nine places for the first letter in the pair; count *back* six places for the second letter in the pair.	(1)
36	b	AY	Count *back* thirteen places for the first letter in the pair; count *forward* seven places for the second letter in the pair.	(1)

For more on answering questions that ask you to find letter analogies, see page 66.

Word analogies

37	**b** wet, **z** dry	Water is wet and dust is dry.	(1)
38	**c** time, **y** length	An hour is a measure of time and a metre is a measure of length.	(1)
39	**b** arm, **x** leg	The elbow is a joint in the arm, and the knee is a joint in the leg.	(1)
40	**b** planet, **z** star	Earth is a planet and the Sun is a star.	(1)
41	**c** multiply, **y** add	You multiply numbers to find their product, and you add numbers to find their sum.	(1)
42	**c** prime, **x** square	Seven is a prime number and sixteen is a square number.	(1)

For more on answering questions that ask you to find word analogies, see page 30.

Find the hidden word

43	c	stop	The door bur**st op**en and the teacher came in.	(1)
44	b	real	They sto**re all** their camping gear in our loft.	(1)
45	c	hear	Dad made **the ar**rangements for our holiday to the seaside.	(1)
46	b	sill	My brother wa**s ill** but he feels much better today.	(1)
47	b	ogre	The fr**og re**turned to the same pond every spring.	(1)
48	c	hero	Gina made **her o**wn way to the school picnic.	(1)
49	a	stow	Thi**s tow**n is full of wonderful things to see and do.	(1)

> For more on answering questions that ask you to find the hidden word, see page 12.

Spot the difference

50 **c, e** **Racquet** and **bat** are items of sports equipment; the other words are the names of sports. (1)

51 **c, e** **Acorns** and **conkers** are types of tree seed; the other words are the names of trees. (1)

52 **b, d** **Glades** and **clearings** are grassy spaces without trees; the other words are names of wooded areas. (1)

53 **b, e** **Contribute** and **converse** suggest a positive conversation; the other words suggest an unwelcome intrusion. (1)

54 **a, d** **Apply** and **exert** do not match the other words, which are related to job opportunities. (1)

55 **a, d** **Wing** and **hospital** do not match the other words, which are related to someone who is looked after by someone else. (1)

56 **b, d** **Cake** and **prize** do not match the other words, which are related to making someone well again. (1)

57 **b, e** **Verify** and **prove** both mean to test the truth of something; the other words relate to beliefs not necessarily supported by evidence. (1)

> For more on answering questions that ask you to spot the difference, see page 28.

Statement logic

58 **c** Although other statements may be true, we do not have enough evidence to prove this. The only statement that must be true is C because we are told that Eddy has maths and history homework. (1)

> For more on answering questions involving statement logic, see page 88.

Match the letter changes

59	c	loop	The first and last letters change places in the second word.	(1)
60	d	caps	The letters in the first word are rearranged in the order 3215 in the second word.	(1)
61	e	note	The letters in the first word are rearranged in the order 4325 in the second word.	(1)
62	d	site	The letters in the first word are rearranged in the order 3245 in the second word.	(1)
63	b	alter	The letters in the first word are rearranged in the order 32567 in the second word.	(1)
64	b	deer	The letters in the first word are rearranged in the order 5623 in the second word.	(1)
65	d	spire	The letters in the first word are rearranged in the order 45376 in the second word.	(1)

> For more on answering questions that ask you to match the letter changes, see page 78.

Basic algebra

66	b	B	$3 + 5 - 4 = 4$	(1)
67	d	D	$12 \div 2 \times 3 - 9 = 9$	(1)
68	d	D	$10 \times 3 + 11 - 28 = 13$	(1)
69	e	E	$4 \div 2 \times 7 + 5 = 19$	(1)
70	d	D	$24 \div 3 + 12 + 3 = 23$	(1)
71	d	D	$16 \div 2 \times 3 + 4 - 14 = 14$	(1)
72	c	C	$36 \div 12 \times 8 + 10 - 22 = 12$	(1)

> For more on answering questions involving basic algebra, see page 56.

Number analogies

73	d	21	Multiply the left-hand side number by the right-hand side number.	(1)
74	c	57	Multiply the left-hand side number by the right-hand side number and then add one.	(1)
75	a	32	Multiply the left-hand side number by the right-hand side number and then subtract four.	(1)
76	b	51	Multiply the left-hand side number by the right-hand side number and then add six.	(1)

77	d	10	Divide the left-hand side number by the right-hand side number and then add two.	(1)
78	c	6	Divide the left-hand side number by the right-hand side number and then subtract two.	(1)
79	b	125	The missing number is the cube of the outer numbers.	(1)
80	a	14	Multiply the left-hand side number by the right-hand side number and then subtract the right-hand side number.	(1)

For more on answering questions involving number analogies, see page 52.

PAPER 3

Move a single letter

1	d	s	Moving the letter 's' from boast to books makes the words boat and books.	(1)
2	d	i	Moving the letter 'i' from plain to star makes the words plan and stair.	(1)
3	c	c	Moving the letter 'c' from focal to hair makes the words foal and chair.	(1)
4	a	g	Moving the letter 'g' from glass to ban makes the words lass and bang.	(1)
5	c	o	Moving the letter 'o' from float to pet makes the words flat and poet.	(1)
6	b	l	Moving the letter 'l' from bleak to mode makes the words beak and model.	(1)
7	d	r	Moving the letter 'r' from shore to bead makes the words shoe and bread.	(1)

For more on answering questions that ask you to move a single letter, see page 14.

Number sequences

8	b	36	The sequence increases by six each time.	(1)
9	a	11	The sequence alternates between increasing by three and decreasing by one.	(1)
10	c	8	The sequence decreases by four each time.	(1)
11	d	1	The sequence counts backwards through the prime numbers.	(1)
12	c	12	The sequence alternates between increasing by five and decreasing by four.	(1)
13	e	64	The second, fourth and sixth numbers are the squares of the first, third and fifth numbers.	(1)
14	c	16	The sequence alternates between counting through square numbers (the first, third, fifth and seventh numbers) and decreasing by two (the second, fourth and sixth numbers).	(1)

For more on answering questions that involve number sequences, see page 54.

Find a common letter

15	e	m	him mat	arm mist	(1)
16	c	g	flag great	rang glade	(1)
17	b	n	barn near	glean nose	(1)
18	e	d	braid dote	glad dine	(1)
19	c	r	poor rain	spear ring	(1)
20	d	l	growl leap	grail lacy	(1)
21	c	r	flour rout	blear raft	(1)

For more on answering questions that ask you to find a common letter, see page 16.

Statement logic

| 22 | c | If it is sunny, Marcus walks to school. We know this because we are told that he usually walks to school unless it is raining. | (1) |

For more on answering questions involving statement logic, see page 88.

Match the meaning

23	b	ring	'ring' is a noun meaning a circle or band; it is also a verb meaning to chime or toll a bell.	(1)
24	d	form	'form' is a verb meaning to make or produce something; it is also a noun meaning a document that you fill in.	(1)
25	d	save	'save' is a verb meaning to rescue or protect something from harm; it is also a verb meaning to reserve or keep something, e.g. saving money.	(1)
26	e	change	'change' is a noun meaning coins or money; it is also a verb meaning to alter or transform something.	(1)
27	e	wind	'wind' is a noun meaning a breeze or gust; it is also a verb meaning to coil or curl something, e.g. a thread. Note that the word 'wind' is pronounced differently depending on the meaning.	(1)

28 **c** pitch 'pitch' is a verb meaning to throw or cast something, e.g. a ball; it is also a noun meaning a place where sport is played, e.g. a stadium. (1)

29 **d** mark 'mark' is a noun meaning a symbol or sign; it is also a noun meaning the grade or rating for something, e.g. a test result. (1)

For more on answering questions that ask you to match the meaning, see page 32.

Join the words

30 **b, z** today (1)
31 **a, y** barrage (1)
32 **b, y** warden (1)
33 **a, z** token (1)
34 **b, x** orbit (1)
35 **b, x** rather (1)
36 **c, y** berate (1)
37 **b, z** legend (1)

For more on questions that ask you to join two words, see page 18.

Deduction

38 **b** Amy Amy has four pets because she has a dog, a cat, a goldfish and a hamster. Beth, Mario, Lee and Carl each have three pets. (1)

	dog	cat	goldfish	rabbit	hamster	Total number of pets
Beth		✓	✓		✓	3
Amy	✓	✓	✓		✓	4
Carl	✓		✓		✓	3
Mario	✓			✓	✓	3
Lee	✓		✓		✓	3

For more on answering questions involving deduction, see page 92.

Letter sequences

39 **d** IG Count *forward* two places for the first letter in the pair; count *forward* one place for the second letter in the pair. (1)

40 **c** UL Count *forward* one more place each time for the first letter in the pair (+2, +3, +4 etc.); count *forward* two places for the second letter in the pair. (1)

41 **c** NI Count *forward* two places for the first letter in the pair; count *back* one place for the second letter in the pair. (1)

42 **d** EP Count *forward* one more place each time for both letters in the pair (+1, +2, +3, etc.). (1)

43 **a** DB Count *back* two places for the first letter in the pair; count *back* one more place each time for the second letter in the pair (−1, −2, −3, etc.). (1)

44 **c** OI Count *back* one place fewer each time for the first letter in the pair (−6, −5, −4, etc.); count *forward* two places for the second letter in the pair. (1)

45 **e** HV Count *forward* three places, then *back* one, then *forward* three, then *back* one for the first letter in the pair; count *back* one more place each time for the second letter in the pair (−3, −4, −5, etc.). (1)

For more on answering questions involving letter sequences, see page 70.

Word relationships

46 **d** lime (1)

    t a l k (f a r e) f i r e   m i n e (l i m e) l a m e
    1 2 3 4 5 2 7 8 5 6 7 8   1 2 3 4 5 2 7 8 5 6 7 8

47 **d** torn (1)

    p l a n (p a l m) m e a n   t r i p (t o r n) n o o n
    1 2 3 4 1 3 2 5 5 6 7 8   1 2 3 4 1 7 2 5 5 6 7 8
              7

48 b main (1)

f a r e (r a i d) r i d e   g a t e (m a i n) m i n t
1 2 3 4 3 2 6 7 5 6 7 8   1 2 3 4 5 2 6 7 5 6 7 8
          5

49 c hart (1)

h e r e (h u r t) s h u t   n o r m (h a r t) t h a t
1 2 3 4 1 7 3 8 5 6 7 8   1 2 3 4 6 7 3 8 5 6 7 8
          6

50 e bowl (1)

p l a n t (p a c k) c l o c k   b r o w s (b o w l) c r a w l
1 2 3 4 5 1 3 6 10 6 7 8 9 10   1 2 3 4 5 1 3 6 10 6 7 8 9 10
           9

51 b hole (1)

s m i l e (m i s t) s t o r m   l i o n s (h o l e) h e a t h
1 2 3 4 5 10 3 1 7 6 7 8 9 10   1 2 3 4 5 10 3 1 7 6 7 8 9 10
        2 6

52 d leak (1)

c r e a t e (c a r e) s p a c e   l a d d e r (l e a k) w r e c k
1 2 3 4 5 6 1 4 2 3 7 8 9 10 11   1 2 3 4 5 6 1 9 2 11 7 8 9 10 11
          10 9 6
             11

For more on answering questions involving word relationships, see page 80.

Word analogies

53 b eye, **x** ear	You see with your eye and hear with your ear.	(1)
54 c plant, **y** brick	Hedges are made of plants and walls are made of bricks.	(1)
55 c plane, **y** train	Planes depart from airports and trains depart from stations.	(1)
56 b fish, **y** bird	Fish are covered in scales and birds are covered in feathers.	(1)
57 a milk, **x** flour	Cheese is made from milk and bread is made from flour.	(1)
58 b waste, **y** grow	If something withers it wastes away; if something flourishes it grows.	(1)
59 b innovative, **z** unoriginal	If something is novel it is innovative; if something is common it is unoriginal.	(1)

For more on answering questions involving word analogies, see page 30.

Balance the equation

60 c 4 (1)

$30 + 6 - 11 = 16 + 13 - \underline{\hspace{2em}}$
$36 - 11 = 16 + 13 - \underline{\hspace{2em}}$
$25 = 16 + 13 - \underline{\hspace{2em}}$
$25 = 29 - \underline{\hspace{2em}}$
$29 - 25 = \mathbf{4}$

61 b 2 (1)

$8 \times 3 + 5 - 2 = 5 \times 5 + \underline{\hspace{2em}}$
$24 + 5 - 2 = 5 \times 5 + \underline{\hspace{2em}}$
$24 + 3 = 5 \times 5 + \underline{\hspace{2em}}$
$27 = 5 \times 5 + \underline{\hspace{2em}}$
$27 = 25 + \underline{\hspace{2em}}$
$27 - 25 = \mathbf{2}$

62 c 0 (1)

$48 \div 12 \times 7 - 1 = 9 \times 3 - \underline{\hspace{2em}}$
$4 \times 7 - 1 = 9 \times 3 - \underline{\hspace{2em}}$
$28 - 1 = 9 \times 3 - \underline{\hspace{2em}}$
$27 = 9 \times 3 - \underline{\hspace{2em}}$
$27 = 27 - \underline{\hspace{2em}}$
$27 - 27 = \mathbf{0}$

63 b 5   (1)

$72 \div 8 \times 5 - 22 = 6 \times 3 + \underline{\hspace{1cm}}$

$9 \times 5 - 22 = 6 \times 3 + \underline{\hspace{1cm}}$

$45 - 22 = 6 \times 3 + \underline{\hspace{1cm}}$

$23 = 6 \times 3 + \underline{\hspace{1cm}}$

$23 = 18 + \underline{\hspace{1cm}}$

$23 - 18 = \mathbf{5}$

64 b 12   (1)

$99 \div 9 \times 4 + 4 = 12 \times 3 + \underline{\hspace{1cm}}$

$11 \times 4 + 4 = 12 \times 3 + \underline{\hspace{1cm}}$

$44 + 4 = 12 \times 3 + \underline{\hspace{1cm}}$

$48 = 12 \times 3 + \underline{\hspace{1cm}}$

$48 = 36 + \underline{\hspace{1cm}}$

$48 - 36 = \mathbf{12}$

65 c 34   (1)

$26 \div 2 \times 4 - 14 = 14 \times 5 + 2 - \underline{\hspace{1cm}}$

$13 \times 4 - 14 = 14 \times 5 + 2 - \underline{\hspace{1cm}}$

$52 - 14 = 14 \times 5 + 2 - \underline{\hspace{1cm}}$

$38 = 14 \times 5 + 2 - \underline{\hspace{1cm}}$

$38 = 70 + 2 - \underline{\hspace{1cm}}$

$38 = 72 - \underline{\hspace{1cm}}$

$72 - 38 = \mathbf{34}$

66 d 10   (1)

$39 \div 3 \times 2 + 16 = 13 \times 4 - \underline{\hspace{1cm}}$

$13 \times 2 + 16 = 13 \times 4 - \underline{\hspace{1cm}}$

$26 + 16 = 13 \times 4 - \underline{\hspace{1cm}}$

$42 = 13 \times 4 - \underline{\hspace{1cm}}$

$42 = 52 - \underline{\hspace{1cm}}$

$52 - 42 = \mathbf{10}$

> For more on answering questions that ask you to balance the equation, see page 50.

Apply the code

67 c	SLQH	Count *ahead* three places in the alphabet.		(1)
68 c	VANW	Count *back* eight places in the alphabet.		(1)
69 c	HOPE	The word is found by counting *back* one place in the alphabet for letters one and three, and two places *back* for letters two and four.		(1)
70 b	TRAY	The word is found by counting *forward* seven places in the alphabet, crossing the end of the alphabet as necessary.		(1)
71 c	UTLGP	Count *ahead* one place for the first code letter, two places for the second code letter, three for the third, and so on.		(1)
72 e	GIFGS	Count *ahead* from the start of the alphabet for each letter, then count *back* the same number from the end of the alphabet to find the corresponding code letter, e.g. the letter T is 20 places ahead from the start of the alphabet, and the G is 20 places back from the end of the alphabet.		(1)
73 b	DRINK	Count *back* one place for the first letter of the word, three for the second letter, five for the third and so on, counting in increasing odd numbers.		(1)

> For more on answering questions that ask you to apply the code, see page 72.

Match the number code

1 = L, 2 = E, 3 = A, 4 = P, 5 = C, 6 = R, 7 = I

The words LEAP and PEAR both share the letters EA in the middle, so the codes with the 23 in the centre must match these words. This enables the letters E and A to be identified in the other words. Three of the words begin with P, and two of the given codes begin with 4, so the code for P must be 4. Only LEAP begins with L, so the code 1234 must match that word.

74 e	4236		(1)
75 b	4712		(1)
76 c	PACE		(1)

4 = E, 5 = R, 6 = M, 7 = A, 8 = T, 9 = O

All the words contain the letter M. M is found at the start of two of the words, at the end of one word and is the third letter in one word. 6 is the only number that matches the position of M in each word. Once the code for M has been found, this enables the code letters E, R, A, T and O to be identified.

77	**c**	MORE	(1)
78	**b**	TART	(1)
79	**e**	69895	(1)

For more on answering questions that ask you to match the number code, see page 58.

Statement logic

80 **d**   Chris is silent for one hour longer than Zoe. We know this because we know that Zoe ends her silence at twelve o'clock, and Chris is silent for three hours (twice as long as Marcus), so Chris ends his silence at one o'clock. (1)

For more on answering questions involving statement logic, see page 88.

PAPER 4
Join the words

1	**c, x**	leaflet	(1)
2	**b, z**	forage	(1)
3	**a, y**	washer	(1)
4	**c, x**	convex	(1)
5	**a, z**	heather	(1)
6	**c, x**	hasten	(1)
7	**b, y**	onion	(1)
8	**a, z**	reapply	(1)

For more on answering questions that ask you to join the words, see page 18.

Word analogies

9	**b** cat, **z** dog	A kitten is a young cat and a puppy is a young dog.	(1)
10	**c** shoe, **y** shirt	A lace fastens a shoe and a button fastens a shirt.	(1)
11	**b** golf, **z** hockey	Golf is played with a club and hockey with a stick.	(1)
12	**b** play, **z** film	You see a play at a theatre and a film at a cinema.	(1)
13	**a** fork, **z** saucer	Knives and forks are used in pairs and so are cups and saucers.	(1)
14	**c** book, **y** money	Libraries lend books and banks lend money.	(1)
15	**a** teeth, **y** bristle	A comb has teeth and a brush has bristles.	(1)

For more on answering questions involving word analogies, see page 30.

Basic algebra

16	**c**	C	$8 + 3 - 9 = 2$	(1)
17	**d**	D	$20 \div 4 \times 3 + 6 = 21$	(1)
18	**e**	E	$10 \times 12 + 5 - 35 = 90$	(1)
19	**c**	C	$60 \div 5 \times 3 - 18 = 18$	(1)
20	**b**	B	$99 \div 11 \times 3 + 8 - 11 = 24$	(1)
21	**e**	E	$36 \div 18 \times 13 + 10 - 0 = 36$	(1)
22	**c**	C	$84 \div 4 \times 3 + 4 - 29 = 38$	(1)

For more on answering questions involving basic algebra, see page 56.

Deduction

23 c George and Lottie   Mia could have her birthday in May or July. Harry's birthday could be in April, June, September or November. George's birthday is in October. The shortest month is February so Ruby's birthday is in December. Lottie's birthday is in October, two months before Ruby's. (1)

	Mia	Harry	Lottie	George	Ruby
January					
February					
March					
April		?			
May	?				
June		?			
July	?				
August					
September		?			
October			*	*	
November		?			
December					*

For more on answering questions involving deduction, see page 92.

Letter analogies

24 d TW   Count *forward* six places for both letters in the pair. (1)

25 b QO   Count *forward* three places for the first letter in the pair; count *back* one place for the second letter in the pair. (1)

26 a VU   Count *inwards* from the ends of the alphabet for both letters in the pair, e.g. count *forward* five places from the start of the alphabet for the letter E, and five places *back* from the end of the alphabet for the letter V. (1)

27 c SM   Count *forward* five places for the first letter in the pair; count *back* three places for the second letter in the pair. (1)

28 e XC   Count *back* six places for the first letter in the pair; count *forward* three places for the second letter in the pair. Counting will cross the ends of the alphabet. (1)

29 b AY   Count *forward* two places for the first letter in the pair: count *back* four places for the second letter in the pair. Counting will cross the ends of the alphabet. (1)

30 d BX   Count *forward* eight places for the first letter in the pair; count *back* five places for the second letter in the pair. (1)

For more on answering questions involving letter analogies, see page 66.

Synonyms and antonyms

31 a close, **y** near   Close and near both mean nearby. (1)

32 b danger, **x** risk   Danger and risk both mean hazard. (1)

33 b flee, **z** escape   Flee and escape both mean to run away. (1)

34 c flaw, **y** defect   Flaw and defect both mean a fault. Note that mend and affix are fairly close in meaning but not the same: affix means to attach something to something else, which is not exactly the same as mending something. (1)

35 a scale, **z** climb   Scale and climb both mean to ascend. (1)

36 b brave, **z** confront   Brave and confront are both verbs that mean to face something challenging. (1)

37 a bright, **y** vivid   Bright and vivid both mean a rich colour. (1)

For more on answering questions involving synonyms, see page 26.

Moving a single letter

38 d s   Moving the letter 's' from clasp to rat makes the words clap and rats. (1)

39 c i   Moving the letter 'i' from chief to pan makes the words chef and pain. (1)

40 b l   Moving the letter 'l' from gloat to mat makes the words goat and malt. (1)

41 d i   Moving the letter 'i' from claim to alas makes the words clam and alias. (1)

42	**d**	r	Moving the letter 'r' from pearl to weak makes the words peal and wreak.	(1)
43	**b**	r	Moving the letter 'r' from grain to bugle makes the words gain and burgle.	(1)
44	**a**	a	Moving the letter 'a' from avoid to repel makes the words void and repeal.	(1)

For more on answering questions involving moving a single letter, see page 14.

Statement logic

| 45 | **d** | Three gifts have spotty wrapping paper. Some of the other statements could be true, but we do not have enough evidence to prove this. | (1) |

For more on answering questions involving statement logic, see page 88.

Apply the code

46	**c**	EQCV	Count *ahead* two places in the alphabet.	(1)
47	**d**	EKGX	Count *ahead* six places in the alphabet.	(1)
48	**b**	VEST	Count *back* four places in the alphabet to find the code; count *ahead* four places in the alphabet to find the word.	(1)
49	**e**	ROPE	Count *ahead* nine places in the alphabet to find the code; count *back* nine places in the alphabet to find the word.	(1)
50	**c**	UTDC	Count *ahead* one more place in the alphabet each time (i.e. +1, +2, +3, +4).	(1)
51	**e**	DEAR	Count in the same number of places from the opposite end of the alphabet (i.e. A = Z, D = W, etc.).	(1)
52	**b**	MINT	Count *back* one more place in the alphabet each time to find the code; count *ahead* one more place each time to find the word.	(1)

For more on answering questions that involve applying a code, see page 72.

Match the number code

1 = F, 2 = R, 3 = A, 4 = I, 5 = M, 6 = E

FARE and MARE have the same three letters at the end, so their codes must be 2326 and 5326. The word RARE has the letter 'R' repeated, so R must be 2, and M must be 5. The word FAIR has two new letters, so its code must be 1342.

53	**d**	2326	(1)
54	**b**	1342	(1)
55	**c**	MARE	(1)

1 = C, 2 = O, 3 = P, 4 = E, 5 = A, 6 = R, 7 = L

CARE and LACE have the same second and fourth letter, so their codes must be 1564 and 7514 (but not necessarily in that order). This must mean that A is 5 and E is 4. CARE and COPE both start with 'C', so C must be 1. The only word with the code 15_4 is CARE, so R must be 6. None of the codes given starts with R, so the code for REAP must be missing. The word with the code 7514 contains the letters _ACE, so 7 must be L.

56	**d**	6453	(1)
57	**b**	34514	(1)
58	**b**	PARCEL	(1)

For more on answering questions that ask you to match the number, see page 58.

Find the hidden word

59	**b**	flea	There was a raf**fle a**t the school fair last April.	(1)
60	**d**	near	We saw an ancient sto**ne ar**ch when we visited Rome.	(1)
61	**b**	pith	My little brother's sand**pit h**as enough room for all of his friends.	(1)
62	**c**	sand	We opened the car window**s and** let in the cool breeze.	(1)
63	**c**	lint	It would be so funny if Dad fel**l int**o the water when we go fishing!	(1)
64	**a**	into	Any ra**in to**morrow could ruin our summer picnic at school.	(1)
65	**c**	mess	Our new puppy someti**mes s**leeps on my bed.	(1)

For more on answering questions that ask you to find the hidden word, see page 12.

Match the letter changes

66 **d** take The third letter is removed and an 'e' added to the end of the word. (1)
67 **b** same The second and third letters are removed and replaced with 'am'. (1)
68 **c** bear The letters in the first word are rearranged in the order 1342 in the second word. Letter five does not appear in the second word. (1)
69 **d** miss The letter 'i' is added as the second letter in the second word. The letters in the first word are rearranged in the order 4(i)51 in the second word. Letters two and three do not appear in the second word. (1)
70 **c** dial The letter 'a' is added as the third letter in the second word. The letters in the first word are rearranged in the order 53(a)2 in the second word. Letters one and four do not appear in the second word. (1)
71 **b** step The letters are rearranged in the order 6451 in the second word. (1)
72 **d** this The letters are rearranged in the order 5426 in the second word. (1)

For more on answering questions that require you to match the letter changes, see page 78.

Deduction

73 **d** 6 (1)

Susie	10 books
Archie	Sam – 3 books = 6 books
Sam	Charlotte + 1 book = 9 books
Charlotte	Susie (10 books) – 2 books = 8 books
Lily	Same number as Sam (9 books)

For more on answering questions that involve deduction, see page 92.

Number sequences

74 **c** 22 The sequence adds one more each time (i.e. +1, +2, +3, +4, etc.). (1)
75 **b** 12 The first, third, fifth and seventh numbers add two each time; the second, fourth, sixth and eighth numbers add three each time. (1)
76 **c** 32 The sequence counts back four each time. (1)
77 **d** 2 The first, third, fifth and seventh numbers count back through the prime numbers; the second, fourth, sixth and eighth numbers add one each time. (1)
78 **a** 18 The first, third, fifth and seventh numbers add four each time; the second, fourth, sixth and eighth numbers count back three each time. (1)
79 **c** 72 The first, third, fifth and seventh numbers count back twelve each time; the second, fourth, sixth and eighth numbers count ahead nine each time. (1)
80 **a** 27 The sequence alternates between adding six and subtracting two. (1)

GL 11+ Verbal Reasoning Practice Papers published by Galore Park